She blazed
with beauty and hunger . . .

"Tyne," Falconer breathed huskily, "do you have any idea what it does to me to see you look like that?"

Her only answer was to touch her mouth to his—in a melting, languorous kiss that sent the blood pounding through her veins. "Show me," she murmured then. "Show me what I do to you."

Falconer's arms closed around her fiercely. Her head fell back as their mouths sipped and tasted and consumed in a fiery prologue to intimacy.

Her hands were tangled in his hair, and a soft, throaty laugh bubbled up in her as he lifted her high in his arms and strode to the spiral staircase. . . .

Undercover

MAURA SEGER

MILLS & BOON LIMITED
15–16 BROOK'S MEWS
LONDON W1A 1DR

First published in Great Britain in 1986 by Mills & Boon Limited, 15–16 Brook's Mews, London W1A 1DR

© Maura Seger 1985

ISBN 0 263 75477 4

21–0586

Printed and bound in Great Britain by Cox & Wyman Ltd, Reading

1

"GET OUT OF THE CAR SLOWLY, miss," the man with the rifle said. "Keep your hands raised."

Tyne Saunders muttered a silent curse as she switched off the ignition. The moonless night and the forest pressing in on all sides made it difficult to see, but she could still discern the three armed and obviously dangerous men who had run her off the road.

They had come upon her a little sooner than she had anticipated, which, all things considered, might be just as well. It was important that she appear properly frightened.

Taking a deep breath, she slid gingerly from the car, her arms raised. With what she hoped was appropriate shock and nervousness, she said, "You're making a mistake. I'm a reporter from the *Financial Times* I'm here to see Mr. Darcourt."

The guard glanced from the slender woman to the two subordinates who had moved up to surround her. He shook his head firmly. "Mr. Darcourt isn't expecting any visitors tonight, miss. If he were, we would have been informed."

Tyne was finding it less difficult to play her part than she had expected. Being on the receiv-

ing end of an automatic rifle had a marvelous
tendency to concentrate one's attention. A cool
wind stirred the oak and pine trees standing
like dark sentinels against the sky and sent a
shiver down her spine. Without lowering her
arms, she managed to shade her eyes a little
from the spotlights trained on her.

"He isn't exactly expecting me." That was a
bit of an understatement. She had no difficulty
imagining what Darcourt's reaction would be if
he knew who she really was and why she had
come.

She didn't want to think about that any more
than she wanted to think about how uncomfortable she was becoming. It had been raining
off and on all day, and the air was chill. Her
thin wool sweater and skirt offered little protection. She was cold, tired, hungry and had no
difficulty sounding more than a little annoyed.

"Don't you think this has gone far enough?"
she added tartly. "After all, I'm hardly a crimi-
nal."

"You've trespassed onto private property,
miss," the senior guard pointed out. "The bor-
ders of Mr. Darcourt's land are clearly posted.
You passed them some time ago."

"It was dark. I . . ."

"Our security cameras picked you up opening the gate and driving through it. Are you
saying that was an accident?"

Tyne managed to feign surprise at this reve-
lation about the security system. She had noticed the cameras as she passed them, but only
because she had known their location in ad-
vance.

"I presumed I must be near Mr. Darcourt's land," she said slowly, "if not actually on it. But I didn't come here intending to do any harm."

As she spoke she managed a weak smile, hoping it would get across to the khaki-clad guards how ridiculous it was to even suspect she was capable of endangering their employer.

Though slightly taller than the average woman, she was softly curved in a way that made her look deceptively fragile. Her face was an almost perfect oval dominated by large thick-fringed eyes that complemented her straight nose with its splash of freckles and her full mouth.

Her unruly red hair tumbling in curls around her head, along with the simple clothes she had worn for her long trip, made her look even younger than twenty-five. All in all, she thought she must present the very picture of innocence.

The guards were unimpressed. Their job was clearly to stop intruders, not to evaluate how dangerous they might or might not be.

"That's not for us to decide, miss," the man in charge said expressionlessly. "I advise you to come along quietly."

Tyne intended to do just that, but she still felt compelled to seem reluctant. "You don't have any right to make me go anywhere."

That was met by stony silence. Her arms were beginning to ache. Curious to see what the reaction would be, she began to lower them.

Instantly the senior guard gestured with his rifle as the two other men stepped closer. "Keep your hands up."

She obeyed quickly, too wise to test them any further. They had their orders, and she had hers. Fortunately there was no need for disagreement, at least for the moment.

"All right," she said. "I won't give you any trouble. But I expect to be taken directly to Mr. Darcourt. Is that clear?"

The man shrugged. "He'll be informed of your presence. When he chooses to see you is up to him."

And that was apparently the best she was going to get. With her hands still raised, she was forced to suffer the indignity of a search, which she had to admit was completely impersonal and over almost instantly.

Good thing she hadn't been so foolish as to carry any weapons on her person, Tyne thought as she was finally allowed to lower her hands. At least the guards didn't insist on handcuffs. Seated in the back of the Jeep with a guard on either side of her, the third driving, she began the final stage of her journey to what was giving every appearance of being a veritable fortress.

The Jeep set off with a lurch, causing Tyne to wince at the banging of her spine against the ill-padded seat. Grimly she struggled against a wave of impatience. Not for a moment did she really believe her presence on this mission was necessary, but she hadn't been able to convince her superiors. They believed Darcourt presented special problems only she could solve.

Served her right for earning a reputation as a thorough-going professional who came through even in the tightest circumstances. Except for that she might have been ensconced back at her house in Connecticut, with nothing to occupy her except her enjoyable job as a reporter with the *Financial Times*. A job that had the dubious benefit of being an excellent cover. Argus had seen to that, as it had seen to so much else.

"Are we going to be there soon?" she asked after they had been traveling for some time. She knew the exact size of Falconer Darcourt's hideaway—five hundred acres—but the guards would expect such curiosity from a nervous and unwilling passenger.

Being well trained, they made no effort to answer her. Instead, as they rounded a corner, she caught sight of...

Tyne blinked hastily. For the first time that evening she was genuinely surprised. Surely that wasn't a ... castle looming before her, complete with stone towers and a moat?

The aerial photos of Darcourt's domain hadn't been good. Taken on short notice some ten days earlier, when his whereabouts had finally been confirmed, they had shown only bits and pieces of his residence between layers of cloud cover.

Since then the weather had remained impervious to even the best efforts of the spy satellite hovering some twenty-two thousand feet above. Reconnaissance planes had flown over twice, with no better results. No one had attempted to subvert a Darcourt employee, since they were known to be unrelentingly loyal. Argus had, however, briefly considered trying to infiltrate an agent onto the property beforehand, but that was rejected as too risky. The organization didn't want to tip its hand.

Therefore, all Tyne had known about her objective was that Falconer lived in a large stone mansion, which she realized now was rather like calling Mother Hubbard's shoe a piece of footwear.

Perhaps the cloud-tossed darkness was making her see things that weren't there. Yet she could swear she was looking at a vast pile of alabaster stone rising gracefully against the sky, seeming almost to float above the pine-spiked hillock it dominated.

It was like something out of a fairy tale, a place for bold knights, fair maidens and dragons. It had no business in the ruthlessly unromantic modern world, but it was, to her startled senses, apparently real.

"This way, miss," the guard said when they had driven over the drawbridge that spanned the moat, then beneath the heavy iron grilles bracketing the narrow passageway leading through the gatehouse. With the grilles raised, a single vehicle could just fit through the stone walls that pressed in on either side. Closed, they would present a formidable barricade, as well as a trap for anyone caught between them.

At the far end of the gatehouse passage, they entered a cobblestone courtyard easily half the size of a football field. Floodlights illuminated the yard and the men moving around it purposefully. Some seemed to be guarding the dozen or so vehicles parked to one side. Others, weapons in their hands, stood on the high crenellated towers that gave excellent views of the surrounding countryside.

Tyne got out of the Jeep hesitantly. What kind of man would choose to live in a castle? For that matter, what was a castle doing in the Hudson River Valley only a few hundred miles from New York City, protected by guards carrying very modern weapons and shielded from the rest of the world by a highly sophisticated security system?

Her head pounding with questions, she followed the silent men through a wooden door studded with iron, down a stone corridor and into a small room that served as an office.

A man was seated behind a gray metal desk. He stood up as she entered and studied her impassively.

Tyne returned his scrutiny. Besides the fact that she needed to get a close look at him, doing so would also make her appear to have nothing to hide. In such situations the subliminal language of gesture and expression had a powerful impact on how a person was perceived, and ultimately treated.

The man was about fifty but in excellent condition, with the rugged, weathered look of one who has been a great many places and done a great many things, some of which he regretted.

His dark hair was slightly thinned and shot through with silver. There were deep lines etched on either side of his narrow mouth and around his steely eyes, which showed not a hint of any emotion as he said, ''I'm Winston Elder, chief of security. Sit down.''

She hesitated before obeying with a hint of relief, a rather nice touch, she thought, and not completely faked. The past week had been long and hard, filled with endless hours of briefings and very little sleep. As a result, she was grateful for the support of the chair.

The security chief leaned against a corner of his desk, with his arms crossed over his broad chest, and continued to regard her steadily.

"Mr. Elder—" she began, coughed to clear her throat and started again. "My name is Tyne Saunders. I'm a reporter for the *Financial Times*. I realize I should have called to confirm my appointment with Mr. Darcourt, but—" her voice gathered strength as she considered how the guards had forced her off the dirt road, brandishing their guns "—but I really must protest the way I've been treated. You have no right to—"

"On the contrary," the large stern-faced man broke in coldly. "We have every right to detain a trespasser. As for your 'appointment' with Mr. Darcourt, we both know there wasn't any. If you are who you say you are, you're just one more overeager reporter trying to get a story. And should it turn out that you aren't even that..."

He let the words trail off meaningfully as Tyne observed him. Winston Elder, whatever else he was, was not kidding. He wasn't about to let her bluff or argue her way out of her predicament. Sighing, she decided on a semblance of candor.

"Look, it's true I shouldn't have come here.

But I did, and now I'm sorry. So either let me see Mr. Darcourt or let me go."

Of the two options, only one was viable. For a moment she thought he might actually be considering taking her to his employer, only to have her hopes dashed as he shook his head. "It isn't up to me to decide. Mr. Darcourt has been informed of your presence. He's very busy now, so I have instructions to make you comfortable."

A slight, chilly smile curved his thin lips. "In keeping, of course, with your . . . unanticipated arrival."

Tyne suppressed a grimace. She wasn't about to let this overgrown crossing guard think he could intimidate her. "Do I have to remind you," she said stiffly, "that it is illegal to detain someone against his or her will?"

With another frosty smile Elder stood up. "I'm sure I don't have to remind you that anyone who puts herself in the position you have risks being dealt with outside the letter of the law."

Walking toward the door, he added, "You are on a large private estate miles from anywhere. I will hazard a guess that at least some of your colleagues knew where you were headed and have some understanding of the difficulty involved in getting there. If you aren't heard from for several days, no one will be surprised."

As he spoke, he was opening the door to the office and gesturing to the guards waiting outside. They entered and stood straight-backed and cold eyed while he gave his orders.

"Escort Miss Saunders to the holding area. She can have whatever luggage is in her car, after it's been inspected."

Turning, he offered Tyne yet another tiny smile. "Dinner will be brought to you. If there's anything else you need—"

"I'd like to make a phone call," she said promptly.

His shrug was eloquent. "I'm sorry, but that isn't possible."

And that was apparently that. The two guards moved up beside her, their grimly purposeful manner leaving her with no choice but to go with them.

Winston watched her leave with narrowed eyes that hid the tumult of his decidedly contradictory feelings. On the one hand, he knew that security requirements demanded she be incarcerated until her identity could be proven, but on the other he couldn't quite ignore the feeling that he was violating the rights of an innocent woman.

Elder nurtured a keen sense of right and wrong, though some who had found themselves in conflict with him would have scoffed at the possibility. His integrity, more than anything else, had led him to his present occupation.

Despite his scruples a sense of unease niggled at the back of his mind. He couldn't quite pin down how, but Tyne Saunders didn't seem exactly as she should.

Perhaps it was just as well that dealing with her from this point on was not part of his job.

He would only advise. Sighing, he picked up the phone, waited for a few moments, then spoke briefly.

HIGH UP in another and far more luxurious part of the castle, Falconer Darcourt nodded as he listened to his security chief's report. As usual, Winston had handled the situation ably.

Falconer said so, then hung up and leaned back in the large leather chair positioned behind a mahogany desk, the focus of the gracefully proportioned room. The wall immediately behind the desk was taken up by built-in bookcases, weighted down not with sterile, leather-bound tomes selected by some anonymous decorator, but with well-thumbed volumes slightly disarrayed by frequent use. On the other side of the room, floor-to-ceiling windows looked out onto a garden obscured by darkness. To the right, there was a large fireplace with a marble mantel. A paneled door to the left led to an anteroom, and beyond to the other parts of the castle.

Amid such elegance, the large rumpled man dressed in corduroy trousers and a plaid shirt might have struck a discordant note. But Falconer Darcourt was completely at ease with his surroundings. He had, after all, created them.

His long legs were stretched out in front of him as he ran a hand through his thick hair, the color of molten gold in the firelight. Tawny eyes were fixed unseeingly on the darting flames.

Something about Tyne Saunders had bothered Winston. The indication had been very faint; nonetheless, Falconer had picked up on it and was curious as to its cause.

He reached into a drawer of the desk and found the file he wanted. Flipping it open revealed a sheaf of letters with a photograph on top, the result of the routine inquiry Winston had made when Ms Saunders's request for an interview at such a critical time had raised some concern. The picture was unposed, taken while she was questioning some dignitary on an airport runway.

Falconer leaned forward, studying the photo more closely. She was interesting to look at. The pale skin and red-gold hair were a dramatic foil for her delicate features. It didn't escape him that her figure was very good, but he was more taken with the expression in her eyes. She was intelligent . . . and determined.

Interesting.

For a moment he was tempted to forget about the work he needed to do in preparation for the next day's meetings and talk with her immediately instead. That impulse faded as quickly as it had arisen. He had a responsibility to the men; they trusted him to see that nothing endangered the vital events transpiring at the castle. No personal consideration could be allowed to intervene.

Sighing, he put the file away and reached for another.

FAR BELOW, in the depths of the castle, Tyne was surveying her new surroundings with the same concentration Falconer had given to her photo.

But in her case she was prompted not by simple curiosity, but also by the knowledge that she couldn't allow herself to remain very long where she'd been put.

The guards had led her down yet another long stone corridor to a small windowless room furnished with a narrow cot and the usual sanitary facilities. A single shadeless light bulb dangled from the ceiling. The door was solid metal except for a grille at eye level, and most definitely locked from the outside. She had heard the bolts slide into place as the men left.

Standing in the center of the cell, her arms wrapped around her, Tyne shook her head wryly. The cell was evidently part of the original castle and might indeed have once been used for very grim purposes. No doubt she was supposed to believe that was still the case, but she didn't.

The dehumidifier near the ceiling gave her the first clue. It was still functioning. Standing on the cot, she examined it carefully, noting that no surveillance devices were planted within. Nor was there a sign of any elsewhere.

Climbing down, she knelt and examined the flagstone floor. At a distance of about twelve inches from the walls, she found tracings of what looked like rust, but upon more careful examination turned out to be particles of wood. Scattered nearby were wisps of dust.

Tyne grinned ruefully. A dehumidifier... wooden racks... dust...? Of course, what better purpose for a cool stone room than to convert it into a wine cellar. Moreover, the flakes of compound around the sink and commode confirmed that the facilities had been recently installed.

Mildly reassured to discover that her "host" was not the sort to have routine need of a cell, she kicked off her shoes and settled down on the cot. With her legs folded beneath her and her hands resting lightly on her knees, she automatically went through the breathing exercises intended to relax and rejuvenate.

Shortly after she finished, a guard arrived with her luggage and a tray of food. He said nothing and left quickly, securing the door behind him.

Tyne eyed the food with interest. A thick ham sandwich on fresh-baked bread and a steaming bowl of homemade vegetable soup made her stomach growl. She made short work of both, along with a tall glass of milk and, for dessert, a very nice custard.

When the food was gone, she settled down to rest. The bare overhead light remained on, contrasting sharply with the absolute silence, but Tyne wasn't troubled by either. With her stomach full, the first phase of her mission successfully completed and no indication that she was in immediate danger, she was essentially content.

After placing a blanket over the grille in the door while she made use of the facilities, she removed it and returned to the cot. There she curled up and was almost instantly asleep.

A guard, passing on routine patrol every half hour throughout the night, observed that the prisoner slept soundly. He made a note in the log to that effect.

BY MORNING Tyne felt thoroughly rested and ready for action. She put the blanket back over the grille while she saw to her morning ablutions, but rejected the idea of changing her clothes. It wouldn't do to look too at ease with the situation.

Shortly after six-thirty A.M., the sound of approaching steps alerted her to the fact that it was time for phase two.

Darting up, she peered through the grille. A young guard was approaching. He was about six feet tall and well built, like all the security staff. On one hand he balanced a metal tray, while the other held the key to her cell.

A possibility, provided she took sufficient care to avoid blowing her cover. If the guard was truly wary of her, he would order her to stand in view before he entered. If he was not . . .

Quickly positioning herself to one side of the door, she waited through seemingly endless seconds, until at last the sound of the key in the lock told her she had a chance. As well trained as he undoubtedly was, still the young man didn't consider her a danger.

That was his mistake, and her opportunity. The door swung open, hiding her as the guard entered. In the microsecond before he could realize the cot was empty, she dashed from behind him and flew out of the cell.

The man's reflexes were good; he turned almost in time to stop her. Almost but not quite.

Even as he was dropping the tray and yelling at
her to stop, Tyne was tearing down the stone
corridor.

She could hear the pounding of the guard's
steps as he raced after her. His shout had alerted
others, who were joining in the pursuit. They
were right behind her and gaining quickly, but
she was in good shape and fueled by determination.

Her long legs flashed in shafts of sunlight as
she raced up stone stairs to a larger corridor.
There she paused long enough to get her bear-
ings. She was in the residential part of the
castle. Luxurious carpets lined the flagstone
floor. Sunlight poured in from clerestory windows near the ceiling and from two immense
bay windows at either end of the hallway. Several simple couches and elegant tables were
scattered along its length. There were bowls of
fresh flowers and paintings she would have
liked to examine more carefully. But not just
then.

A half-dozen heavy wooden doors lined the
corridor at intervals of ten to fifteen feet. Most
probably opened onto guest rooms, which
weren't what she was looking for. The sound
of pursuing footsteps reminded her she had to
make a choice quickly, and that it had better be
the right one.

A door at the far end of the hallway was set a
little apart from the others. That, coupled with
the fact that the room behind it would be on a
corner with more windows and the best view,
decided her.

Darting behind the door, she resisted the urge to slam it, knowing the sound would alert her pursuers. She eased it carefully shut and leaned into it heavily, her lungs straining for air and her heart pounding. On the other side she could hear the guards racing by, their boots thumping against the stone floor.

When they were gone, she breathed in deeply. Her leg muscles felt as though they were on fire, and her whole body trembled. There was nothing like a few days in the field to banish any idea of being in good shape.

Glancing around, she took in the large chamber that was her temporary sanctuary. Like all the rooms she had encountered so far in the castle, it was walled in stone, with a high, arched ceiling, leaded windows and a flagstone floor. One entire side of the room was taken up by a large fireplace that faced what had to be the most enormous bed Tyne had ever seen.

It stood on a slight dais reached by two steps, the frame hewn of oak and polished to a deep golden gloss. The bed was covered by a burgundy velvet spread that matched the canopy draped overhead. On either side hung tapestries that, even to Tyne's inexperienced eye, looked to be of museum quality.

The rest of the furniture in the chamber was simple but elegant: a table on which lay, incongruously, an open file and a calculator; several high-backed chairs padded in rich black leather; and a carved chest below a wall display of crossed lances.

On closer study she noted small personal

touches—a beautifully carved ivory unicorn perched on a small shelf in a recess, a collection of books, a mandolin propped against one wall—all of which reassured her she had guessed right.

There was a closed door at the far side of the room. A shaft of light shone under it. From somewhere behind that door, a phone rang.

It was answered on the first ring; a deep voice murmured something, paused, murmured again. Tyne heard the click as the phone was put down, and the further click as the door opened.

She counted to three, then whirled and grabbed for the door handle even as she heard the startled exclamation of the man behind her.

2

Falconer had been astonished to learn of Tyne Saunders's escape from the holding cell. It suggested that she might indeed be far more dangerous than anyone had seriously thought. The precautions taken with her the previous night were, with hindsight, more than justified.

A search was already under way, which he had intended to join. Until he walked into his bedroom and found the object of all the furor crouched against the door.

Tyne's efforts to get the handle unstuck were proving futile, of course. While she continued to try, she glanced swiftly over her shoulder. What she saw brought her up short. The few blurred photos she had seen of Falconer Darcourt hadn't done him justice.

He was very tall, well over six feet, and clearly in superb condition, with broad shoulders, a solid-looking torso, narrow hips and long legs.

The skin, stretched over facial bones that held a hint of Viking origin, was tanned to a healthy bronze that emphasized the golden tints in his hair. Incongruously, it occurred to Tyne that he didn't bother to get it cut very often.

The thick, slightly tangled mass of amber

curls suited him. It went with the leonine glitter of his eyes. Eyes that were locked squarely on her.

Whatever surprise he might have felt at discovering a flushed, disheveled woman pressed against the door of his bedroom, he controlled it admirably as he said, "Ms Saunders, I presume?" His voice was deep, slightly husky and ominously gentle, as though he didn't mind at all how much his sudden appearance frightened her.

It was that last part that restored Tyne to herself and reminded her of who she was supposed to be. Pulling furiously at the door, she at last managed to get it open and was about to dart through it when a large, burnished hand slammed the door shut again before closing on her shoulder.

"Don't you have any sense at all?" the man demanded gruffly as he whirled her to face him. "You can't possibly get away."

That showed what he knew. Time for Mr. Darcourt to find out he had more on his hands than he thought.

"Challenge him," Argus had directed. "He responds to that." It would be her pleasure to carry out those instructions to the letter.

Grasping his large wrist in both hands, she twisted slightly, levered his weight over her right hip and in the next instant discovered she had lost none of her judo skills.

The man landed with a dull thud on his back and lay ominously still, his amber eyes closed and his big body limp.

Tyne stared at him warily. Not for a moment did she believe he was really hurt. She had known exactly what she was doing when she threw him, applying neither too much nor too little force. But the person she was supposed to be wouldn't realize that. She would fall for the little trick he was playing.

Hardly breathing, she inched closer to him. The rise and fall of his broad chest was barely discernible, and he still hadn't moved. With appropriate hesitancy, she knelt beside him and reached out to find his heartbeat.

She never got a chance. There was a blur of motion, and Tyne was hauled unceremoniously against him. Both her hands were instantly captured behind her, held effortlessly by one of his, while the other tangled in her unruly titian curls and jerked her head back.

His face was only inches from hers as he demanded, "What now, Ms Saunders? A knife in the ribs, or something even more effective? I imagine you weren't searched very thoroughly."

A fact he was clearly intent on remedying. Tyne's gasp was quite genuine as a big hand moved determinedly over her breasts, pausing in the cleft between them before continuing over her slender waist and flat abdomen to her thighs.

"Stop it!" she protested fiercely as every muscle in her body stiffened rebelliously. "You don't have any right to do this!"

He ignored her objections and completed the search with infuriating thoroughness. Only then did he frown as though perplexed. "No weapons. Why did you come back at me?"

Because I knew what you were playing at and decided to go along. "Because I thought you were hurt, you idiot! And I was stupid enough to want to help you. Now let me go!"

Falconer's frown deepened. Her claim was inconsistent with both her escape from the cell and her knowledge of self-defense. Yet she had exhibited none of the more deadly skills of unarmed combat, which jibed with her lack of weapons.

"Winston thinks you may really be who you claim," he said slowly. "I'm not so sure. You've got a lot of explaining to do, and I suggest you be quick about it."

Tyne did not take well to being ordered around by any but Argus. Moreover, she didn't like being manhandled, especially when she couldn't respond with the full force of her considerable ability.

Instead she was getting an object lesson in how an ordinary woman felt when confronted by the greater strength of a male determined on bending her to his will. From some deep, previously untapped source within her resentment rose, sharp and bitter.

To give in to him was not only inconsistent with her instructions, it was utterly unthinkable. Without pausing to even consider the consequences, she brought up her knee, hard.

This time she lacked the advantage of complete surprise; he managed to pull away and deflect the blow. But in doing so, his balance gave, just enough for her to wrench her hands free and yank herself away from him.

She was racing for the door even as Falconer jackknifed to his feet and reached for her. All thought of restraint was gone as a sinewy arm — honed by hours of practice with weapons that demanded both immense strength and skill — coiled around her waist.

Tyne cried out as the world turned upside down; shattered seconds passed before she realized she had been tossed over a broad shoulder and was being carried across the room.

Her senses spun again as he released her, dumping her in the center of the huge bed. She had barely an instant to gasp for breath before his powerful body, tense with anger, came down on top of her.

Her hands lashed out at him, only to be caught and manacled by his as he pulled her arms above her head. The movement pressed her high, full breasts, only lightly covered by a thin sweater and bra, against his broad chest.

Falconer stared down at her, the blood pounding in his ears and his own breathing none too steady. He kept trying to remember that she was an intruder, possibly dangerous, perhaps even deadly. Somehow he couldn't quite keep that in mind. The feelings she aroused astounded him.

He was a civilized man who prided himself on his self-discipline, yet he was suddenly behaving like a rampaging Viking. That might have been funny, had he not been so thoroughly in the grip of forces he couldn't control.

Her resistance fell like tinder onto reactions

that were already flaring out of control. His touch had abruptly changed. From wanting initially only to subdue her, he was now driven to do far more.

The movements of her slender body as she struggled under him made him vividly aware of every inch of her, from her breasts surging against him to the slender curve of her waist and the ripeness of her hips pressing into his. Their legs were intimately entwined, his holding hers apart in a position far more common to lovers than enemies.

Ruefully he acknowledged that there were times when the line between the two became blurred. He was suddenly, acutely aroused. A fact which didn't escape her notice.

He watched with satisfaction as her remarkably blue eyes widened and a wash of color stained cheeks soft as the petals of a rose. A low chuckle broke from him.

"Ms Saunders," he murmured huskily, "or whoever you really are, I hope you know what you've gotten yourself into."

Tyne was suddenly all too aware of that. She went absolutely still, watching him with frozen disbelief as slowly, unrelentingly, his head bent to her as he released her hands.

The touch of Falconer's mouth on hers was unexpectedly gentle. She had instinctively been prepared for roughness, but this sensual exploration caught her completely off guard. Drawn irresistibly to coax from her a response equal to his own, he tugged gently at her lower lip, his tongue darting out to trace the inner moistness.

Tyne gasped brokenly. Bewildered by the sudden shock of pleasure, she redoubled her struggles. But without forgetting who and what she was supposed to be. Above all, she had to convince him of that.

Such sharp little fingers, Falconer thought idly as he at last raised his head. His high-boned cheeks were slightly flushed, his tawny eyes glittering like topazes lit by an inner sun.

He had learned what he had set out to, and a bit more. Quietly he said, "Your repertoire is limited."

Tyne's mouth fell open. She had the distinct suspicion she should feel insulted, but wasn't sure why. "W-what do you mean?"

"If you were really a terrorist, or someone of that ilk, you'd have a wider range of defense moves," he said matter-of-factly. "Instead it seems you haven't progressed past the basics." He added, "Unless you're a better actress than I realize."

"Thanks very much," Type snapped, galled. "I happen to have been first in my judo class."

He might have laughed except that he imagined her self-control was hanging by threads, hardly surprising considering what she had been put through. If she really was innocent, she had every right to be upset about being confined for a night, hunted down by armed guards, then more or less attacked by a man many times her superior in size and strength.

Remorse, a most unusual sensation for him, caused him to seize her hands gently as he removed them from his hair. Still holding them, he said, "All things considered, it would have been simpler to just grant you an interview. Now that you're here, perhaps we should discuss it."

Tyne blinked at him in pretended astonishment. "*You're* Falconer Darcourt?"

He grinned crookedly and made no effort to release her as he said, "Let me guess; I'm not living up to your expectations."

"Y-you're . . . too young to be him." About thirty-five by her guess, which even she found remarkable if he had really accomplished all he was credited with.

"Nonsense. I've just made very good use of my time."

At such close quarters, the smile he shot her was devastating, combining as it did complete awareness of her predicament with the unmistakable suggestion that given half an ounce of encouragement, he would not be averse to staying exactly where he was and pursuing the encounter to its logical conclusion.

When Tyne refused to blink this time, he sighed in mock resignation. Without taking his eyes from her, he released her and stood up. The hand he held out to her was ignored as she quickly scrambled off the bed on the other side.

Shrugging, he reached for a phone in a wooden cabinet. Her gaze was locked on his as he spoke into it. "Tell Elder to cancel the alert. She's here." He listened for a moment, then said, "No, I'll take care of it."

When he hung up, he said calmly, "You've ruined Winston's day, not to mention the guard's.

It will be a long time before either of them forgets this." He smiled suddenly. "Neither, for that matter, will I."

Tyne was hard pressed to feel any sympathy for the security men, or their employer. The large bed positioned between them, the dark spread rumpled, reminded her all too vividly of her unwelcome response to Falconer.

She was embarrassed by it and didn't hesitate to lash out at the source of her uneasiness. Frostily she said, "I have a little trouble being concerned about that, considering that I've lost track of the number of laws that have been broken by people acting in your name."

At his raised eyebrows, she acknowledged, "I'm convinced you really are Darcourt. If you weren't, you wouldn't have been able to call off security. I don't imagine Winston Elder would accept instructions from anyone else. The point is that you seem to think you can do anything you like—but you're quite wrong about that."

Her brave words belied the tremors of surprise she was still experiencing as she confronted the man who watched her so intently. As he came around the bed to face her, she had to fight a very unprofessional impulse to retreat.

His unruly amber hair was still slightly damp from a recent shower, and his skin glowed with vibrant good health. He moved with animal grace as he narrowed the space separating them.

Tyne gulped inwardly but put up a valiant front. So what if she was forbidden to make use of her skills until the moment was right. She could still hold her own, couldn't she?

Falconer frowned as he looked down at her. She was pale, and the shadows under her eyes reminded him of where she had spent the previous night. To his surprise, something inside him flinched at the thought. He was not generally a man who quailed at doing what was necessary, no matter how tough that might be. Though he understood why rigorous security was vital under the present circumstances, he regretted any discomfort she had been caused. And he wanted very much to make up for it.

"Have you eaten anything today?" he asked quietly.

It was working; he was beginning to see her as simply a hapless victim of circumstances beyond her control. Carefully, not wanting to appear too eager, she said, "I . . . didn't hang around for breakfast."

Falconer frowned again. "I think we'd better get some nourishment into you." Sternly he added, "You look as though a puff of wind would knock you down."

Her head snapped back, her eyes darkening to the shade of a storm-tossed sea. "Don't patronize me. I'm not some little airhead incapable of taking care of herself." At least that was true, even if she did say it only for effect.

No, Falconer thought on reflection, she wasn't; that delectably curved body housed an unexpectedly strong will. But not even she could ignore the effects of what she had been through, though she was certainly trying.

"Let me put it this way," he said patiently. "I am about to have lunch, and I would like you to join me. All right?"

Tyne hesitated for the space of a breath. Things couldn't have been working out better, so why was she uneasy? Her orders were to stick as closely as possible to Falconer, never mind the unexpectedly personal implications of that.

Falconer watched the play of emotions across her face and was troubled by it. He wanted to tell her she had nothing more to be frightened of, but he knew that would be a lie.

She was wise to be so wary. In the space of a few brief moments, she had unleashed something in him that he could scarcely credit, let alone understand.

His gaze drifted to the shadowed hollow at the base of her graceful throat, and he caught himself wondering what it would feel like to press his mouth there.

He had been without a woman for a long time, by his own choice, but nonetheless with the predictable effects. His self-control, generally so dependable, was suddenly precarious. He would need very little encouragement to find himself making long, sweet love to her. Which might be fine, except that afterward there would be consequences to deal with that could complicate matters already complicated enough.

Resignedly he settled for a less dramatic choice. "There's no doubt that we've gotten off—shall we say—on the wrong foot. I suggest we start over, by sharing a meal."

A shopworn phrase so popular among certain types of urban professionals flitted through Tyne's mind: *let's have lunch sometime.* Superficial, noncommittal, safe.

She could use a little safety. Just for a change.

With considerably more savoir faire than she was feeling, she shrugged. "All right, as long as you have someplace in mind other than that horrible cell."

"I think we can do better than that," Falconer murmured as he opened the door and stood aside to let her pass.

A short time later they were seated on a terrace with a breathtaking view of the Hudson River Valley. As Tyne drank in the beauty of verdant hillsides burgeoning with the promise of spring, a waiter poured sparkling mineral water into crystal goblets, while another set out a basket of French bread fresh from the oven.

Sensing Falconer's eyes on her, she felt constrained to add, "This is all quite lovely. Rather . . . different from last night."

"I'm sorry about that. I hope you understand that strict security precautions were required until we determined who you really are."

Tyne did, though she wasn't about to admit as much. Instead she said, "I can assure you I really am a reporter. And I don't mean anyone any harm," she added for good measure.

He studied her for a moment before nodding. "I was ready to believe that, based on the information Winston confirmed about you. But your expertise at self-defense literally threw me."

Despite herself Tyne felt the corners of her mouth curving up. "You recovered very well."

Spearing a sliver of honeydew melon, he asked, "Have you been studying judo very long?"

"A few years. It's good exercise. Besides, living alone as I do, it's nice to know something about taking care of myself." Her half smile faded into a convincing grimace. "Much good that it did me."

He had the grace to look abashed. "Don't be too hard on yourself. I've had considerably more experience with such things." His amber eyes darkened slightly. "I hope I didn't hurt you?"

The brief reference to his own skill in unarmed combat did not elude her. There were gaps in the dossier on Falconer Darcourt, big ones. So long as she was on the job anyway, it wouldn't hurt to try to fill them in.

He could have damaged her badly had he wanted to, and she would have been powerless to stop him without blowing her cover. Instead she was certain she had come away from the encounter without even a bruise. At least physically. Those moments in his bed had sparked an inner turmoil she was having a great deal of difficulty coping with.

In an effort, most likely futile, to distract herself, she said, "No, not at all. Besides, I was much more concerned last night when it seemed as though I had fallen into the clutches of a paranoid hermit."

His laughter was rich and full, startling in its spontaneity. A waiter standing at a discreet distance looked up suddenly before glancing quickly away. The gesture was enough to tell Tyne her mysterious host did not laugh very often.

"And now," he was saying, "you're vastly reassured."

This time her smile ran its natural course, bringing a teasing light to her sapphire eyes. "Well...no, not vastly. Let's just say I'm no longer convinced you're crazy."

He raised an eyebrow eloquently. "You still think it's a possibility?"

"Why not? It's a crazy world."

His expression sobered as a member of his staff filled crystal glasses with fresh orange juice. When they were alone again, he said, "I can't argue with that any more than I can try to convince you of my sanity." A lighter note entered his voice. "Perhaps you should just take me on faith."

Tyne sniffed delicately. No halfway sensible woman would do any such thing, as he undoubtedly realized. Any man living in a looking-glass world of medieval castles and space-age security systems would inevitably arouse great curiosity.

"If you had really wanted to avoid attention from people like me," she pointed out, "you should have made yourself seem ordinary and uninteresting. You've done just the opposite."

"Why do you say that?"

She shot him a chiding look. "Your seeming obsession with privacy, for one thing, not to mention your—shall we say unusual?—life-style."

"I suppose you mean the castle."

"It does tend to set you apart. Tell me, did you build it or have it moved here from Europe?"

"Neither. I would consider either action absurdly extravagant."

At her startled look, he grinned. "There's a fine line between individuality and eccentricity. To the best of my knowledge I don't cross it."

"Then how . . . ?"

"Several years ago I was camping in this area—I do that occasionally to relax—and happened upon the castle purely by serendipity. It struck a chord in me, so I made inquiries and learned that it had been brought over here from Normandy in the nineteenth century by a railroad baron who fancied himself a feudal lord. His heirs had long since put it on the market, but there were no takers."

He winced slightly. "It wasn't hard to see why. The place was a wreck, but I suppose I was in the mood for a challenge, because I decided to try restoring it."

Tyne nodded slowly. "You've certainly succeeded. The castle is breathtaking."

As he acknowledged the compliment, she added, "And from a strictly pragmatic view, I suppose it does offer a fair amount of protection and privacy."

"That's generally the case." Crêpes stuffed with thin slices of ham were set before them. He went on matter-of-factly, "Only very rarely does anyone actually set foot uninvited on my lands, and then its usually by accident. Intruders are dealt with quickly and effectively."

Tyne paused in the midst of taking a bite. Ever cursed by an overly active imagination, she couldn't help but blanch. He smiled in gentle rebuke and explained, "They're escorted off the property."

She relaxed a fraction, only to stiffen again as she wondered why she was being treated differently. Somehow Argus had known she would be, perhaps not so surprising a perception, considering that the organization was named after the hundred-eyed creature of Greek myth. "Why wasn't I? I did offer to leave."

Falconer hesitated. He wasn't sure how to answer her question. Strictly speaking, when informed of her presence he should have ordered her immediately shown off the estate.

Instead, he had directed Elder to have her brought to the castle, with the result that he confronted the problem of what to do with her.

"I was aware that you wanted an interview with me," he said slowly, "and I was . . . curious to meet you. I've read quite a few of your articles. They impressed me."

Tyne didn't even try to hide her surprise. She was always a little self-conscious about meeting someone familiar with her work, which was silly considering that she knew how large the circulation of the *Financial Times* was and should have long since grown accustomed to a minor celebrity status in business circles.

But somehow the thought of Falconer reading her articles made her at once pleased and anxious. What did he really think of them?

The question must have been in her eyes, for he smiled with unexpected gentleness. "You have a talent for making the people you write about leap off the page. I've finished your articles feeling as though I've actually met the person even when I haven't. In those cases where I've known whoever you're writing about, I've invariably gained new insights and understanding."

Tyne was at a loss to respond. He had touched the very essence of what she tried to do, to communicate something about one person to another. And he had told her she succeeded.

"Thank you," she murmured. "I've never claimed any great insights into the financial world, but I do care about people." She might have been better off otherwise.

"That's obvious, and I suppose it's why I wanted to meet you." Finishing his meal, he regarded her steadily. In his eyes was the memory of how she had felt beneath him, all softness and vulnerability.

There was more than just that behind his attraction to her: the knowledge that her mind was capable of clear, clean insights and the dawning awareness that she was imbued with some special quality, or combination of qualities, that sliced straight through all his carefully constructed defenses to the inner man.

With rather explosive results, he thought ruefully, considering his actions in the bedroom. Watching her, he wondered how she felt about that. Was he correct to think there had been something in her response besides perfectly justifiable anger and fear? Or was he fooling himself, reading into her small, subtle signals a complexity of feeling that matched his own?

Tyne bore his scrutiny silently. Rather to her surprise, it didn't disturb her. She knew she was hardly looking her best in wrinkled clothes, with her hair uncombed and her face bare of makeup. But that didn't seem to matter.

Instinctively she understood that facades meant nothing to Falconer Darcourt; he saw through them with practiced ease. Fortunately her true self was buried so deeply as to be invisible. At least so she hoped.

When they had both finished their meal, he rose and held out a hand to her. "Let's take a walk."

Automatically she placed her hand in his and stood up. His touch was warm and gentle with an underlying firmness that made her feel oddly protected.

Strange thought. She had learned at the tenderest age not to expect protection from anyone. It was a source of pride that she needed no one to look after her, and she most certainly did not need any untoward feelings for this man. They would only complicate a job that already promised to be difficult enough.

So why was she looking up at him as though he held the key to some great mystery?

Lowering her eyes hastily, she strolled with him along the balcony above the Hudson. The day was turning warm, though not unpleasantly so. She felt comfortably relaxed, to such a degree that it took her a moment to recognize the sensation. Barely had she done so when it faded.

"I'm having your luggage moved to guest quarters," Falconer was saying as he squinted into the sunlight, watching something in the trees on the hillside. "You'll be more comfortable there."

"That presumes I'm staying."

He turned back to her, his face carefully expressionless. "You have to. I can't permit you to leave."

3

"I REALIZE how much you value your privacy," Tyne said tartly, "and I certainly don't want to do anything to upset that. But there is such a thing as freedom of the press, not to mention personal liberty. If you insist on keeping me here, you'll be violating both."

"I know," Falconer murmured, surprising her by his directness. "And I don't like it a bit. But I can't see that I have any choice."

Before she could interrupt, he went on, "Surely it's occurred to you that the security surrounding the castle is unusually heavy, to say the least. There's a very good reason for that, a reason you may have already discovered."

His gaze narrowed on her. Her wide blue eyes looked genuinely puzzled, yet he couldn't be sure. After her escape from the cell, she had been free for about a quarter of an hour. During that time she might have seen or heard something that could reveal the truth of what was going on in the castle.

"The risk that you might have discovered what's happening here is simply too great," he went on quietly.

"I don't understand what you're talking

about," she insisted. "I haven't discovered anything."

"Perhaps that's true. If I were thinking only of myself, I'd give you the benefit of the doubt. But there's far more involved. Either you agree to stay, or I'll have to notify certain people of your presence and let them decide what to do."

At her quick, apprehensive look, he added, "Not that they would hurt you, but you would certainly be confined on some pretext or other. At least here I can offer you more pleasant accommodations and the interview you said you wanted."

"I still do," she pointed out hastily, "but it seems to have a high price attached to it. You're asking me to relinquish my freedom for some reason you won't explain."

"Not until you agree to my terms. Since there is a chance you haven't realized what's going on, I'm certainly not about to tell you until I can be sure of your cooperation."

"It sounds as though I can't win either way," she pointed out tightly.

"You can look at it like that," Falconer acknowledged. "Or you might consider that you'll simply be taking the opportunity to do in-depth research on the story you said you wanted, namely me."

The sharp glitter in her light blue eyes made it clear she wasn't going to make it that easy on him.

Reflecting ruefully that the lovely, wary young woman before him was a hard bargainer, he tried again. "Suppose I can work out a deal whereby you get first crack at the story of what's happening here, once it's ready to be released. Would you go for that?"

Tyne made a show of thinking it over. His suggestion fell in perfectly with her objective of sticking close to him. The promise of not one but two major stories was simply icing on the cake.

"All right..." she said slowly, "if you can work that out, I'll go along. But there are limits to my patience. I'm not about to sit on ice for very long, and I'll hold you to your promise of an interview." Her slender shoulders rose and fell in wry acceptance. "Heck, if these mysterious goings-on continue long enough, I might get a whole book out of this."

He grimaced. "Surely no one is that interested in me."

She shot him a skeptical look. Did he really not understand the extent of the curiosity he provoked? As though his business dealings weren't enough to make people hungry for information about him, his elusiveness made him all the more irresistible. The fact that he had managed to guard his privacy for so long was testimony to both his tenacity and his power.

Through a unique set of circumstances, she happened to be the one who would finally puncture the wall of mystery surrounding him. Doing so would be both a professional triumph and a personal challenge.

It would also be very dangerous.

With characteristic honesty, Tyne didn't try

to evade the knowledge that—from the first instant she had set eyes on Falconer, she had felt intensely attracted to him. Why, precisely, she didn't know. Whatever was happening between them was at so deep a level as to defy analysis.

For the moment, at least, she was simply going to have to ride with the current, and try not to think too much about where it might be going.

Clearing her throat, she asked, "Now will you tell me what's happening here?"

He looked at her thoughtfully. "After you've had some rest."

Correctly anticipating her protest, he added, "It's a safe bet that you had a difficult night, not to mention the shock of being chased by my guards. Besides, if I'm going to level with you, I've got to clear it first with some other people. So please, Tyne, indulge me and give yourself a break."

His use of her given name, added to the intimacy of his smile, made her rethink her instinctive refusal. The truth was she needed some time alone to plan her next moves. Anyway, though he had the wrong impression of how she had spent the night, a little extra rest wouldn't hurt her.

A warm bath followed by a nap would be not only enjoyable but also highly sensible. Having agreed grudgingly to his suggestion, she was escorted by a solicitous servant to her new quarters.

The room, or more correctly, the suite she had been allocated was almost as large as Falconer's own, which, she couldn't help noticing, was only a few doors down the corridor. But while his quarters were impeccably masculine, these were undeniably feminine.

An antique Aubusson carpet in muted tones of mauve and ivory lay over the polished oak floor. Tables inlaid with ivory bracketed a bed draped in diaphanous curtains and covered by a beautifully embroidered silk spread.

The same pattern of needlework was picked up in the pillows covering the window seat. The room overlooked a garden where daffodils and dogwoods were just beginning to bloom.

Adjacent to the bedroom was a bath as large as the first apartment Tyne had been able to afford on her own. It included a sunken marble tub surrounded by flourishing ferns, a double shower stall and a steam cabinet. Next to it was a dressing room complete with fitted closets and drawers that could easily have held ten times her entire wardrobe.

Shaking her head bemusedly, she began the usual careful inspection of her surroundings. Once again, no surveillance devices were in evidence. But she did uncover what she had really been looking for.

Somehow—she knew better than to ask how—Argus had found a way to get a weapon to her. It could only have been placed there recently, after Darcourt had given instructions for new accommodations to be prepared for her, yet it was exactly where she had been told to look. A panel at the back of the closet proved to be loose; behind it she found what she was looking for.

The small automatic pistol with silencer was thoroughly familiar to her. Nonetheless, she checked it over carefully, along with the extra ammunition clips, before replacing the panel. From now until the mission was over, she would be armed.

Only then did she undress and hang her clothes away while noting that her luggage had already been unpacked. With nothing else demanding her immediate attention, she slipped into the hot tub someone had thoughtfully run for her.

She had seen many servants since arriving at the castle, but in addition there seemed to be an entire, invisible army of them. Surely nothing else could account for the multitude of small and large touches that together created an environment of unbridled graciousness and comfort.

Leaning her head against the padded rim of the tub, Tyne sighed contentedly. For just a little while she was content to forget where she was and why. It was enough to simply let her mind drift while the tension eased from her body.

At length, when her knees began to feel like jelly and her skin was distinctly pruney, she rose, dried herself on one of the thick, soft towels and slipped on a robe.

Padding into the bedroom, she discovered that in her absence another member of the invisible army had dropped by to turn down the

bed and leave a tray of fruit juice and ice on the
table beside it.

A woman could get very used to being treated like this, she thought a little wistfully, even
as a small voice in the back of her mind sternly
warned her that the castle and everything in it
was no more than a romantic indulgence on the
part of a man who could well afford to amuse
himself in so fantastical a way. Rather than be
swept up by the storybook setting, she had to
concentrate on the harsh reality it hid.

And that meant studying the file that had also
been concealed behind the panel. It contained
the latest update on the situation from Argus —
terse and to the point — reminding her that
nothing mattered except the mission.

After having committed the file to memory,
Tyne carried it to the bathroom and placed it in
the sink. The paper was a special compound
that dissolved when exposed to water. Within
minutes all evidence had been destroyed.

That done, she lay down for a brief rest. To
her surprise, by the time she awoke the sky, vis-
ible through the open windows, had turned
softly blue and mauve with the fading day. The
faraway call of a night bird reached her on a
caressing breeze. She could smell the fresh
scents of pine and hemlock, cool stone and polished wood. All distractions she couldn't afford.

Half an hour later, when Tyne descended
from the second floor of the castle, she was informed by a steward that cocktails were being

served in the gallery. Arriving there through a set of floor-to-ceiling doors framed on either side by huge pots of hothouse geraniums, she found what looked like a full-blown dinner party in progress.

There were about a dozen guests, all male, clustered around two men she had no difficulty recognizing.

The U.S. secretary of state and the royal foreign minister of the Kingdom of Bahdai were supposed to be on opposite sides of the world, or so recent statements from their respective press secretaries had claimed. Instead they were very much together, each nodding as the other spoke, amicability evident between them.

For years the United States had been trying to negotiate the right to maintain a military base in Bahdai for use if trouble broke out in the Middle East. The kingdom's leaders had resisted the idea, but recently there had been signs they might be willing to agree.

Even if Tyne hadn't been so thoroughly briefed, she would have immediately recognized the nature of the meeting going on within the walls of Falconer's castle. She managed, nonetheless, to look properly surprised.

Across the room, Falconer suppressed a wry smile as he watched the silent evidence of her surprise, recognition and finally wariness. He hoped they were all genuine reactions. In the hours she had been asleep, Winston hadn't been able to turn up anything to indicate she was other than what she claimed, a very persistent reporter. But doubts still lingered. Not enough, however, to distract her host from other, more pleasant thoughts.

Falconer had considered Tyne lovely from the first, but now she was even more beautiful. The teal-blue knit she wore lent her an air of sophisticated elegance while clinging lovingly to her curves. Her magnificent titian hair was swept up into a mass of curls, framing her oval face and revealing the slender purity of her throat. The total effect was of delightful femininity and grace.

Her arrival had caused a quick change of atmosphere. Conversations broke off abruptly as hard eyes fastened on her, asking unmistakable questions: who was she, what was she doing there, had security been breached?

With a word to the man he'd been chatting with, Falconer excused himself and strode across the room. Tyne stopped where she was and watched him.

Impeccably dressed in evening clothes, he still looked ruggedly masculine, an aura of barely restrained virility and power clinging to him. The easy strength with which he moved reminded her of a great hunting animal, not anything confined to the land, but a mighty bird that could soar on the wind, surveying its domain with tawny eyes. Whoever had given him his unusual first name must have had a premonition of the man he would become.

So caught up was she in studying him that she gave no thought to the tableau they presented.

Even in such "civilized" times, every other man in the room instinctively recognized and acknowledged Falconer's dominant position. His wealth was only the outermost indication of his aggressive nature, a combination of intelligence, will and a vision of what he wanted to achieve that made him a leader among leaders.

It was only to be expected that such a man would have a woman of great beauty and sensuality.

When he reached Tyne's side and smiled down at her, there was a certain protectiveness in his manner. And when he took her hand in his, he was, quite knowingly, announcing his claim on her.

The other men understood this, though Tyne did not. Just as deep undercurrents could flow between women without ever being decipherable by the opposite sex, so could men share the same silent, instant communication.

She knew only that Falconer's look and touch made her acutely aware of the two of them while blanking out almost everything else. Considering how often her life had depended on her ability to properly perceive a situation, that was a galling admission.

Whatever was happening between them, it made her acutely uneasy. She was determined to overcome this obstacle.

Falconer's attitude didn't help. His smile deepened, spreading to his amber eyes as he murmured, "I'm glad I gave instructions for you not to be disturbed. The rest must have done you good. You look exquisite."

The compliment took her aback. It was so . . . courtly. The men she knew didn't talk like that. They either mumbled inarticulately or acted as though feminism had made such niceties obsolete.

Even as she struggled to come to terms with the odd sensations his praise set off in her, she had to admit she liked this new-old way of doing things.

And she liked the security she felt as she moved, on Falconer's arm, into the gathering.

The surprise at her presence began to die down swiftly. Falconer could sense silent questions giving way to acceptance as the men supplied their own answers. He was gratified, and not a little relieved.

As long as the matter of her identity was being settled, he wanted to keep her out of the hands of the federal agents who would be understandably concerned about any breach in security. The simplest way to do that was to provide an explanation for her presence that would put her beyond suspicion. Hence his care to give the impression that there was a special, even intimate relationship between them.

Yet he had to admit that as logical as his actions might be, he had another, deeper motivation for them. He rather liked the idea of truly having such a claim on Tyne. To begin with, she was far more than simply beautiful. The sharp, articulate intelligence she showed in her writing attracted him greatly, as did the compassion and sensitivity he sensed lurking beneath the surface.

Such gentle qualities had been lacking in his life for a very long time. In the struggle first to survive and then to control, he had given their absence little thought. Until he had walked into his bedroom and found a startled ginger kitten with wide eyes and ruffled fur looking for all the world as though she had run to him for safety.

With a small shake of his head, he considered the foolishness of that. Introducing her to his guests, he couldn't help but be aware that Tyne was a self-possessed woman, capable of handling herself well under difficult circumstances.

She greeted each man with a pleasant smile, engaged readily in chitchat and slipped smoothly into the high-powered, elite gathering.

When the formalities had been observed and he was at last able to steer her toward the bar, Falconer said quietly, "I'm sorry I didn't think to warn you about this, but I must say, you seem very much at ease."

Tyne accepted a glass of Pinot Chardonnay from the bartender. "My work has accustomed me to mingling with all sorts of people, Mr. Darcourt, although—" she smiled faintly at him over the rim of her glass "—I have to admit I was a bit startled to find myself in such exalted company."

"They're just people like everyone else," he said, swirling the ice cubes in his Scotch and soda. "Admittedly with more serious problems and responsibilities. Their meeting here is very important."

She nodded, turning to survey the men. Conversations had resumed, but she sensed she and Falconer were still a subject of great interest. "The secretary of state looks tired."

Falconer glanced in the official's direction and nodded. "Hiram is worn out. He's been on the go for months now, with little to show for it so far. Not that Shakir has had it any easier. Being foreign minister of Bahdai is no picnic."

"How do you come to know these men so well?"

"My companies do a fair amount of business in the Middle East. Inevitably, that means making political contacts. And given that region's importance to our own country's security, it's not surprising that I've become acquainted with diplomatic officials here, as well."

It was a sensible, even believable explanation, but hardly complete. Surely there were many other businessmen in similar positions, not as powerful as Falconer, certainly, but also not without influence. Why had he, out of them all, been chosen to host such a vital meeting?

"They must trust you a great deal..." she ventured carefully.

"We share the same objective, peace." Almost as though he thought that sounded too altruistic, he added, "War is bad for business."

Provoked by his cynicism, Tyne shot back, "Not if you trade in armaments."

"I don't." He grimaced slightly. "Despite what you may have heard, I also don't deal in drugs, military secrets, black-market babies, nubile young females or stolen gems. My businesses are distressingly ordinary."

"Oh, come now. I'll admit information on Falconer Enterprises is hard to come by, presumably because you prefer it that way. But most informed people I've spoken to estimate your personal fortune at well into the millions. That's hardly ordinary."

"Don't be misled by the magnitude of what I do. I started out with almost nothing and built my companies stone by stone, contract by contract. The fact that I've been successful hasn't changed the fundamental attitudes I began with."

"So you're saying that you were always scrupulously honest, and because of that men like the secretary of state and the foreign minister trust you with their secrets?"

Falconer looked at her for what seemed like a long time. "Have you always been so suspicious?" he asked softly.

"I'm not," she insisted automatically. "My line of work has naturally taught me to be cautious about what I believe, especially when dealing with strangers."

His brooding expression soon lightened, giving way to an engaging and utterly suggestive smile. Dropping his voice to a murmur, he said, "You can hardly consider us strangers."

Unspoken was the reminder of the intimacies they had shared, and of how close they had come to so much more.

Warmth crept over her cheeks as she recalled that scene in his bedroom all too vividly. "Mr. Darcourt," she said firmly, "you may find it amusing to play games, but I assure you I don't. Being locked in that . . . dungeon last night didn't put me in the best of moods. We'll get along much better if you'll remember that I'm a reporter here to do a job.''

The Scotch had suddenly lost its taste for him. He sighed deeply and put it down as he looked at her. The hint of genuine hurt in his eyes surprised her. It was gone in an instant, making her think her mind must be playing tricks on her. Surely so assertive and self-possessed a man could not possibly care what she thought of him.

Falconer told himself he was a fool. He shouldn't be disappointed simply because she had the same view of him as everyone else. After all, he hadn't given her any reason to think differently.

For that matter, why should he want to? He had long ago become aware of the value of maintaining a certain image, aloof, impenetrable, even mysterious. Hence his refusal to have anything to do with the media, despite the clamoring for information about him.

What right did he have now to complain because the results no longer suited him?

Tyne was looking up at him warily, her light blue eyes guarded by thick lashes. Moments passed, yet she apparently felt no need to speak. Silently she waited for him to do so.

A beautiful woman wise enough to know when to say nothing was a formidable adversary. If he was like most men, he would fall all over himself trying to impress her, to banish the caution he sensed in her and win her full approval.

But Falconer Darcourt was not in the least like other men. Among other traits, he knew when to keep his own counsel and how to bide his time.

4

THE DINNER held to celebrate the successful conclusion of one phase of the treaty negotiations was as lengthy and lavish as might be expected.

Adjacent to the gallery was a long, high-ceilinged chamber that in another era might have been a lord's great hall. It was furnished with a table covered in linen and large enough to easily seat the approximately three dozen guests. Chandeliers of bronze and pewter hung at intervals from the ceiling, their diamond brightness reflecting off the beautiful place settings of rare crystal, china and silver.

Uniformed stewards worked with silent efficiency beneath the ever-watchful eye of a majordomo as meals fit for kings were unfolded course by spectacular course.

Seated across the table from Falconer, between a gentleman from the State Department and a member of the Bahdai royal court, Tyne tried to give the proceedings the attention they deserved. She was continually distracted by the enigmatic man who had so swiftly and decisively imprinted himself on her mind and body.

To his left sat Hiram Griswald, secretary of state and rumored to be a possible future presi-

dent. To his right was Prince Abdul Shakir,
foreign minister of Bahdai and heir apparent to
the throne of that ancient kingdom.

Yet there, in a transplanted medieval castle
hidden from the rest of the world, they seemed
at ease and unmistakably grateful to the man
who had brought them together.

As Falconer's easy laugh reached out to caress her, Tyne tuned out the State Department
man's amusing anecdote and watched the play
of light on golden hair and bronzed features.

Amid the luxury and elegance of the setting,
he was like a . . . She stopped, drawn up short by
her inability to relate him to any of her previous
experiences.

The simple truth was that he resembled nothing and no one she had ever encountered. If he
had, even fractionally, she might have been able
to cope with the effect he had on her, to dismiss
it as a result of the traumatic events of the past
day.

Instead she was vividly aware that she and
Falconer had only just begun to cross swords.
He challenged her in the most fundamental
ways possible, upsetting all her preconceived
notions about the appropriate behavior of a
late-twentieth-century woman confronted by
late-twentieth-century man.

Not that she had anything against that particular species; for the most part he was an
agreeable enough sort. Not for the world would
she want to exchange him for the macho males
of less enlightened eras. Only occasionally did
she allow herself to wonder where all the ex-

citement, the thrills and chills—in a word, the romance—had gone.

Romance. She turned the word over in her mind. There had been singularly little of that in her life. If pressed, she would have to admit that she doubted it really existed. And yet...

Smiling absently at the man next to her, who took that as encouragement to begin still another tale, she considered the man whose amber gaze touched her from across the table and made her forget, momentarily, all else but his presence.

Mingled resignation and exhilaration rippled through her as she met his eyes. His were dark with banked flames only waiting to spring again to life, while hers were clouded as if by winds whipping up to storm force.

For an instant torn out of time they confronted each other, a man and a woman communicating without words the hunger inexorably drawing them closer and closer.

The instant passed; the world fell back into place around them. Amid the murmur of voices and the clink of crystal, the scents of flowers and wine and rare spices, the dazzling colors of light broken by a thousand prisms, Tyne struggled to regain control of herself.

A butter-soft sliver of beef filet was served to her. She ate it automatically, even as she sipped the perfectly aged Bordeaux that gleamed like spilled rubies and exchanged pleasantries with the prince of Bahdai.

Yes, indeed, New York was splendid for shopping, but for serious indulgence you couldn't beat Rome. Certainly Impressionist art remained an attractive investment, yet the primitives were definitely gaining in popularity.

The best restaurant in the world ... ? Well, everyone had an opinion about that, but there was a little place she knew snuggled way in the hedgerows of Normandy.

Falconer was watching her again, not even making an effort to hide his scrutiny. Abdul, so rapt in his attentions, caught the glimmer of topaz eyes and momentarily hesitated.

He had been vaguely entertaining the thought that Falconer might be willing to share his lovely mistress. That clearly was not the case.

The State Department man, no slouch in the deciphering of silent signals, also caught the look, and his attitude toward Tyne took a subtle shift, prudence winning out over valor.

Irked by the deep currents she sensed but could not quite grasp, Tyne hid her apprehension behind gaiety. She smiled and nodded and engaged in the meaningless but nonetheless amusing point and counterpoint of social repartee, all with more success than she could have imagined.

Abdul Shakir blinked, no doubt rather dazzled. The State Department man took a deep swallow of his wine. She was beautiful, vibrant, utterly feminine and quite devastatingly charming. A seeming innocent playing with weapons she did not really understand.

Falconer watched the scene with great enjoyment. She was, he decided, like swift-running water splashing blithely in the sun, ignoring the rocks beneath.... All golden music and light-filled song, wild flowers blooming on an end-less summer day and the froth of sea waves cresting on a distant beach.

His hand, dark against the snow-white cuff of his shirt, closed on his wine goblet, but he didn't raise it to his lips. No wine, however rare and rich, could surpass the taste of her mouth or the fragrance of her skin. Reluctant though he was to admit it, he was already beginning to suspect that no food, however superb, could satisfy the hunger within him.

Dessert arrived at last, mounds of raspberries glistening with sprinkled sugar, velvety choco-late and brandy-laced cream, fingers of airy al-mond wafers—all accompanied by champagne sparkling in fluted glasses and a fine liqueur that rolled on the tongue like liquid gold.

Tyne tasted, sipped, swallowed, sensations like showers of light coursing through her. Un-knowingly she parted her lips, the tip of her tongue catching between white teeth.

She wanted— No, she wouldn't think of that. Better to concentrate on what she needed— No, that wouldn't do, either.

She should—that was it—she should leave, find some place where she could be alone to re-cover the equanimity that seemed to be desert-ing her so speedily.

The men leaned back in their chairs, expan-sive in the aftermath of the delicious meal. The stern-eyed butler in swallowtails approached with a silver tray on which rested a selection of cigars.

He looked to Falconer for guidance, who in turn looked to her. Softly, as though even his voice should touch her only as a caress, he asked, "Would you mind if we smoke?"

Such an archaic question, reeking of vanished days when the ladies judiciously retired, leaving the gentlemen to their port. Yet, under the circumstances, not a bad idea.

Struck by a vision of herself surrounded by clouds of odiferous smoke and sleekly content men, Tyne shook her head. "Not at all, but if you don't mind, I will excuse myself."

Before he could comment, she rose, and wonder of wonders in this day and age, the entire company rose with her. An adroit waiter sprang forward to remove her chair as benign smiles fell on her like soft spring raindrops.

Smothering a sigh at the tendency of the male to backslide into such endearingly chauvinistic practices at the drop of a cigar ash, she met Falconer's gaze, finding it amused yet gentle.

For the space of a heartbeat she held his eyes; then the heat became too much and she looked hurriedly away.

The butler bowed her out through the double doors to the main hall with its marble staircase curving up out of sight. Behind her, as the doors closed, she heard the resumption of conversation.

At the foot of the stairs, she hesitated. A brace of iron-studded portals stood barely a dozen yards from her. Beyond lay the cobblestone courtyard wreathed in evening's darkness and farther on, the gates and the winding road leading from the castle back into the world.

A world whose harshness was set to intrude at any moment. Somehow she had to remember that and not allow herself to become distracted by thoughts of the soaring power of a falcon's wings against a mythical sky, or the untrammeled perfection of a unicorn in full gallop across a meadow of dreams.

Myths and dreams, the stuff of fantasy. Knights of old and maidens fair, fire-spouting dragons and winged griffins, love and honor under an ageless sun. Illusion and wistfulness meeting in the hidden places of the mind. They had nothing at all to do with reality.

So what, a tempting voice whispered as she entered her room and shut the door, finding the curtains drawn and the bed pulled down, fresh flowers on the nightstand and a negligee laid out for her.

It all seemed real enough, solid stone and gleaming silk, fragrant hyacinths and crackling fire. A place carved out of wishes that murmured on the night, filling her with visions of fanciful longings and impossible dreams.

Tyne shook her head dazedly, aware suddenly that she was very tired. The strain of pretending to be something she wasn't had taken its toll. Her arms were leaden as she removed her gown and hung it away, then unfastened the holster she wore around her thigh and slipped it, with the gun still inside, under her pillow. Only then did she remove the rest of her garments.

So tired... She sighed gratefully as she stretched out in the bed, reaching with a bare arm to switch off the light and pull the covers over her.

The night air wafting through the high windows was perfumed with the scents of moist air, new leaves and pine. She breathed in deeply and snuggled farther under the covers, never knowing when consciousness slipped away and she yielded to the embrace of sleep as though it were a lover.

HOURS LATER, when the final wisps of cigar smoke had faded and the last swirls of brandy had vanished, Falconer said good-night to those few of his guests who hadn't already retired and made his way to his quarters.

His black velvet evening jacket hung open, revealing the long, taut expanse of his chest. He had undone his tie and opened the top buttons of his shirt. A triangle of burnished skin dusted with golden curls shone against the pristine whiteness.

One hand was in the pocket of his trousers, perfectly tailored to the narrow line of his hips and sinewy legs. With the other he absently rubbed the back of his neck.

It was very quiet in the house, by his standing order, all the servants were in bed. He had never seen any reason for them to wait up until whatever capricious hour the revelries ended.

He walked quietly, with the supple grace of a man at ease in the depths of the forest. His footsteps made no sound down the long corridor, past the watchful eyes of carved Madonnas, the flicking glances of fair maidens, and the haunting scrutiny of valiant knights.

Faith, love, honor, the tripod on which humanity perched. He possessed the first and third, but not the all-essential ingredient in the center.

His pace slowed as he neared Tyne's door. He paused and looked steadily at the polished oak barrier separating him from her.

Or was she really there? No alarm had been given by security, but that didn't necessarily mean anything, since Tyne had already managed to elude his guards once.

His hand settled on the bronze door handle. Slowly he eased it open and soundlessly pushed in the door.

It was very dark in the room, but his tawny eyes adjusted quickly. Taking a step inside, he shut the door behind him and stood looking at the bed.

A slim, soft mound beneath the covers proclaimed her presence. Stifling a sigh of relief, he moved closer.

She slept with the innocence of a child, one slender arm flung out in disarray and her glorious hair spilling across the pillows. Her thick lashes cast shadows over her damask cheeks; her moist lips were slightly parted.

Carefully, determined not to wake her, Falconer bent down beside the bed and studied her lingeringly. Even in sleep, the vibrancy of her personality was not completely hidden. He could sense it in the deep, steady rhythm of her breathing, in the slight flush of her petal-smooth skin and in the warmth of her slender body reaching out to him.

Unbidden, the memory of how it had felt to hold her beneath him tumbled through his mind. He backed away slightly, knowing that to remain too close was to risk tempting himself beyond endurance. The forces she unleashed in him had been severely restrained for too long.

His hand reached out to gently brush away a curl drifting across her brow. He had already felt the unwilling response of her body; soon, he promised himself, he would know her complete acquiescence and eagerness.

"Soon," he whispered on the night air. Beneath his touch, prompted perhaps by that single, murmured pledge, she stirred restively.

Falconer removed his hand and stood up, without taking his eyes from her. A while longer he watched as she settled back into sleep with a slight smile curving her enchanting mouth.

Her dreams, whatever they might be, seemed pleasant. He envied her that, since he suspected his own sleep would be anything but easy. As he left the room, closing the door carefully behind him, he told himself that would not last long.

Soon, before the harsh light of reason could intrude on the magic being spun out between them, he would make her his.

It didn't escape Falconer's notice that by doing so he would also be placing himself in her

care. The thought of such vulnerability made
him flinch.

In the day-to-day running of his businesses,
he thought nothing of taking risks that would
make other men pale. But this was different.
The business was his shield, the armor hiding
his inner self. In his personal life, he had no
such protection. That was why he had always—until now—been so careful to avoid
emotional commitments that could end in disappointment and pain.

Reaching the privacy of his own quarters, he
undressed and stood for a brief time at the open
window overlooking the night-shadowed hillside. Far below, the dark silver ribbon of river
was winding through secret glens and around
deep crevasses.

The cool, slightly damp air touched his naked
body without his feeling it. He was caught up in
other thoughts, of silken skin and umber hair,
brave eyes and honeyed lips.

Wryly he smiled into the night. He was revealing a hitherto unexpected talent for the po-
etic. It remained to be seen if he would also turn
out to have a talent for wooing a skittish young
woman too wise in her innocence to be swayed
by anything less than truth.

Or if he would be deceived by his own unful-
filled dreams, and find not love but betrayal.

TYNE OPENED HER EYES after he'd left. She had
come instantly alert the moment he entered the
room, but had carefully concealed that. His ac-

tions troubled her, all the more so because she had enjoyed his nearness and his touch.

She sat up and rubbed the back of her neck, tense from the effort of holding still. Her throat was unexpectedly tight, and a weight seemed to be pressing down on her chest. It took her a moment to recognize the outward symptoms of an emotion she had not allowed herself to experience in many years: loneliness.

Lying down again, she slipped a hand under the pillow and felt the cold barrel of the gun. It reminded her of who she was and why she couldn't afford the luxury of ordinary human feelings under these circumstances.

Still holding on to it, she slipped back into sleep.

5

"THE SITUATION HERE is not exactly what I had expected, Chauncey," Tyne said as she sat cross-legged on her bed the next morning. The dignitaries had departed for their respective capitals to report on their progress, so that the castle was unusually quiet.

On a tray beside her were the remnants of a pot of coffee, fresh-squeezed orange juice and flaky croissants. She was struggling without too much success against the seductive feeling of being pleasantly coddled, trying to concentrate on all she hoped to accomplish that day.

"It's going to take longer than I thought to get the story," she added.

"Take as long as you need," Chauncey agreed, blithely managing to sound as though he had never in his life bitten off the head of a writer for being a few hours late with a story, never mind the days or weeks Tyne was asking for. "It's fantastic that you've gotten in there and actually met the great man himself. No sense blowing it by trying to rush him."

Tyne smothered a sigh. She could picture Chauncey leaning back in his big leather chair with his feet propped up on his paper-strewed desk. The huge plate-glass window with a view of the New York skyline loomed behind him; the busy city room of the *Financial Times* stretched straight ahead. He was a compilation of so many contradictions that it was hard to anticipate how he would react to any given situation.

Part dandy, part hardworking newspaperman, he had the wardrobe of an extremely successful male model and the mind of a computer. On the far side of forty, he looked ten years younger, except around his hazel eyes, which had seen too much of the world's pain and couldn't help but reflect it.

Yet for all his innate compassion, he never hesitated to drive his reporters to their absolute limits in pursuit of the news.

Tyne had prepared herself for the possibility that he would kick up a tremendous fuss at the delay, in which case she would have to stall him. Instead he was positively purring over the prospect of her getting the story, no matter how long the assignment took.

"I'm glad you understand," she murmured. "A less thoughtful editor might object."

He brushed that aside with a flick of his Ivy League drawl. "Nonsense. You do a splendid job, and we both know it. If it takes you longer than usual this time, not to worry. Besides, I hear Darcourt's estate is magnificent. You might be able to combine the trip with a little vacation. Wouldn't that be nice?"

"Just peachy. I'm not in the mood for a vacation."

"Now, now, you know what they say about

all work and no play. It wouldn't hurt you to relax for a while.''

"Where was this attitude when I wanted to go to the south of France for a few weeks last year?''

"That was different. We needed your story on the OPEC leaders.''

"How about the vacation I had planned to Mexico?''

"It conflicted with that Common Market meeting.''

Damn Chauncey, he had an answer for everything! Moreover, mention of the OPEC and Common Market stories reminded her of Argus missions she had carried out during both, all the while pretending she would rather have been on vacation.

The duplicity had never bothered her before, but it was beginning to. If she talked to her editor much longer, the entire day would be ruined. She preferred to reserve that privilege for Falconer, who had such a knack for setting her on edge.

"I've got to go now. With luck I'll be in touch again soon.''

"Fine. Whenever you're ready. Oh, give my regards to your host.'' He chuckled indulgently. "That is, if you can remember to do so. I imagine he's rather distracting.''

"He's just another job,'' Tyne muttered, and hung up, staring off into space with a very glum expression on her face. Would that that were true. The short time she had spent in Falconer's domain had taught her that he wasn't just another anything.

Unfolding herself from the bed, she headed for the shower, determined to banish all thoughts of her host. It didn't quite work out that way. The sensuous touch of warm water flowing over her naked body awakened languid memories of how it had felt to be held in steely arms against a rock-hard chest.

"Oh, Lord," she sighed. She was getting as bad as some giddy adolescent in the throes of her first crush. This really had to stop. Stepping from the shower, she dried herself hastily, then grabbed a brush and blow dryer to try to work some order into her unruly hair.

Half an hour later she emerged from her room dressed in elegant blue-gray slacks and a mauve silk shirt, chosen because they reminded her that she was very much a successful professional, more than able to cope with whatever outlandish surprises life chose to throw at her.

As Tyne made her way down the corridor, that resolve weakened slightly. She was struck by the disconcerting sense of being transported into another world. Falconer had assembled a collection of medieval art that was quietly evocative of a bygone age, in which chivalry and courage had been the keystones of life. Yet it had also been a time of immense violence and treachery.

Which side represented the true nature of Falconer Darcourt? Deciding seemed increasingly important to her, for reasons that had nothing to do with the article she would write about him.

Deep in thought, she followed the curving stone staircase down to the central hall. In response to her inquiry, a polite servant indicated that her host was taking his morning exercise.

Following directions, she strolled through the large formal gardens behind the castle, where tame peacocks roamed, and found the gravel path leading to the tennis courts and swimming pool.

Hardly in keeping with the medieval setting, she thought wryly. Falconer might have a keen appreciation for the past, but that didn't prevent him from enjoying the best the present had to offer—while no doubt keeping as astute an eye on the future.

Several tables were scattered around the pool, including one already set for breakfast. Tyne took a seat there and glanced with what she hoped was convincing casualness toward the man cutting a sleek, swift swath through the sun-dappled water.

Falconer moved with extraordinary grace and power, the muscles of his back and shoulders bunching and relaxing rhythmically. His tawny hair was a gleaming pelt clinging to his well-shaped head. He might have been a creature of the sea instead of a man, so perfectly did he fit his environment. Which was hardly surprising. Falconer would dominate any setting; that was simply his nature.

She had no idea how many laps he had completed before she arrived, and she lost count of how many more he did. Just watching him was exhausting; his energy was indomitable, as was his strength.

At last he stopped, not because he gave the slightest sign of being tired, but apparently because it was time to do so. Resting his arms on the side of the pool, he shook his head to clear the water from his eyes and pulled himself easily out of the pool.

Tyne stared unabashedly. The sight of his magnificent body rising nearly naked from the water caused her awareness of anything apart from him to evaporate.

He wore only brief black swimming trunks that did nothing to disguise the powerful sweep of his tautly honed form. He might have been an athlete in peak condition, rather than a businessman who spent a large portion of his life behind a desk.

His massive shoulders and chest, glistening in the sun, riveted her gaze, as did his sinewy thighs beneath narrow hips minimally covered by the trunks. There could be no doubt about his masculinity. Her lips parted soundlessly as she wrenched her eyes from him, praying he hadn't noticed her preoccupation.

If Falconer was aware of his impact on her, he gave no sign of it. Briskly he dried himself, donned the terry-cloth robe a servant held for him and settled himself at the table across from her as she finally remembered the glass she was holding and shakily put it down.

"Did you sleep well?" he inquired politely as a waiter arrived with a silver coffeepot.

Tyne refused a cup; she had already had quite enough stimulant.

Having assured Falconer that she had slept soundly, she asked, "Do you...uh...always start the day so energetically?"

The corners of his mouth quirked up. "If I don't get enough physical activity, my work suffers."

"Oh...." The thought of what other sorts of physical activity he undoubtedly enjoyed made her blush, so rare an experience for her that it took a moment before she realized the significance of the warmth creeping over her cheeks.

She made a determined effort to change the trend of the conversation. "I spoke with my editor this morning. He's very excited about the interview."

Falconer raised an eyebrow. "As he should be, since I've never consented to one before."

"Yes...well, naturally he's eager to have it completed as soon as possible." That wasn't quite what Chauncey had said, but she was reasonably certain he would prefer the story done quickly.

Rather than responding directly, he gestured toward the waiter returning with a tray. "Will you join me?"

Ever the perfect host, Tyne thought sardonically. "No, thank you. Your staff is very thoughtful. I had breakfast in my room."

He nodded and waited until his own meal had been placed in front of him and the waiter had again withdrawn before he said casually, "I wouldn't advise your editor to plan on going to press immediately. The negotiations are proceeding on schedule, but they'll still take some time to complete."

Having dropped that in her lap, he took a bite of the omelet, succulent with melted cheese and bits of herbs.

Tyne's mouth tightened. She didn't want to admit that she was apprehensive about what would happen if she stayed too long in his company. "How much time?" she asked, willing herself not to show her concern.

He swallowed and shrugged lightly. "It's hard to say—a few weeks, perhaps."

Though she would have liked better news, Tyne wasn't surprised. Such delicate diplomatic dealings customarily took as long, or longer. Reluctantly she refrained from muttering any of the sharp words that sprang to mind. Long moments passed; suddenly Falconer chuckled.

The sound startled her, and she made the mistake of glancing in his direction, only to have his gaze catch and hold hers.

"You really are an astonishing woman, Tyne Saunders." He shook his head. "So cool and collected on the surface, the perfect self-sufficient career woman. While underneath . . ."

His voice trailed off as he surveyed her appreciatively. Tyne promised herself that this time she was absolutely, positively not going to blush. She didn't keep her promise.

"How old are you?" he demanded abruptly. "Twenty-two or three?"

Indignant, she shot back, "Twenty-five, not that it's any of your business."

"Of course it is. Surely you didn't expect to learn all about me without my getting to know you?"

Actually, she had expected something like that. It was par for the course for reporters to study and analyze their subjects without opening themselves up to the same scrutiny. "I don't see why you should want to. After all, once I leave here it's unlikely we'll ever see each other again."

Distracted by the dismay the thought caused her, she missed the shadow that darkened Falconer's eyes, which vanished as he shrugged. "That may be, but it makes no difference. I want to know about you, so you will oblige me by answering my questions."

Feeling for all the world as though she was some object trotted out for his amusement, and not wanting to think about why that hurt her so much, she retorted, "Don't count on my obliging you with any answers. I can always say 'no comment.'"

He smiled imperturbably. "That's your privilege. I have other sources to satisfy my curiosity."

"Other? You mean you'd have me investigated?" Much good it would do him. The truth about her was buried beneath so many layers of duplicity and deceit that she had almost lost track of it herself.

Falconer had the grace to look embarrassed. He was already checking up on her, determined that whatever his personal inclinations, security had to be protected. Still, he could hardly tell her that.

"As I said, I'm curious about you," he said slowly.

For a moment Tyne studied him silently. She had caught his careful evasion of her question and understood what it meant. Oddly enough, she couldn't manage to get upset about the fact that he'd ordered at least some scrutiny of her. Perhaps because she was beginning to understand how intensely he valued his own privacy and how thoroughly she had intruded on it.

"Since it seems I'm going to be here for a while," she began, "I guess there's no harm in our getting to know each other." A small laugh escaped her. "Provided, that is, that you aren't expecting too much. I hardly think I'm the most interesting person in the world."

"I'll be the judge of that," Falconer muttered. Spearing a slice of fresh pineapple with his fork and placing it on his plate, he said, "So you're twenty-five. How long have you been a writer?"

"Twenty years."

"What?"

His surprise made her laugh. Catching him off guard, even in so small a way, was a victory of sorts. "My first opus was written in red crayon and dealt with the trauma of starting kindergarten."

"You mean you could read and write when you were five years old?"

"Yep, it was quite a shock to realize other kids

couldn't. Of course, when my teachers found out they were very perturbed. I hadn't learned by the proper methods, you see."

He laughed appreciatively. "Yes, as a matter of fact, I do. Until my family transferred me to a more, shall we say, enlightened school, I had similar experiences."

"It's hard to imagine you going through things like that," she admitted candidly.

"Surely you're aware of the fact that I was once a child?"

His sarcasm made her flush. "Of course, it's just that—" She broke off, knowing there was no adequate way to explain how difficult it was to see him as anything but the indomitable man he had become. Instead she asked, "Where did you go to school?"

He named several of the most exclusive and respected private academies in both the United States and Europe. That didn't surprise Tyne, but his answer to her next question did.

"What about college? Ivy League, I suppose?"

He hesitated a moment. "No, actually I never went to college."

Now that was unusual. Young men from wealthy families—and his must have been to send him to those schools—always went on to get advanced degrees.

"What happened?" she asked gently, realizing it was a very sensitive topic.

He took a sip of coffee and sat back in his chair, regarding her steadily. His scrutiny lasted so long that she had begun to think he had decided against telling her. Abruptly he said, "My father died the month before I was due to start at Princeton. Immediately after his death various stockholders in the company, most of them relatives, joined with a competing firm to try to force a merger. I knew that was the last thing my father would have wanted, so I attempted to stop them. Unfortunately I was too young and inexperienced to succeed. They got the company, and I ended up with the rare privilege of starting all over again in the world."

His matter-of-fact tone suggested that what he had been through was nothing out of the ordinary, when in fact the opposite was clearly the case.

Chewing on her lower lip, she considered what it must have felt like to be an eighteen-year-old boy confronted by the twin blows of his father's death and his relatives' betrayal. Somehow he had found the courage and skill to achieve immense success.

There was so much more she wanted to know, but the tightness of his mouth and the shadows in his amber eyes made her uncustomarily hesitant. She sensed that he had already revealed much more of himself than he had planned, and that if she tried to force the issue he would undoubtedly draw back. Better to wait until he was less on guard.

Her eyes were pensive as she studied the man across from her, glimpsing in him a vulnerability she hadn't expected and that, by contrast, made his strength and will all the more evident.

Her instinctive response was to do something, anything to ease his pain.

He awoke a depth of yearning she had never quite felt before, making her vividly aware of a vast, untapped portion of herself only waiting to be released. The knowledge was at once frightening and exhilarating.

Tyne understood, though she couldn't have said how, that potent magic was at work—it had to be handled with great care. It wouldn't do to hurry anything, nor was there any reason to try. Soon enough reality would come to the castle high above the winding river.

6

"YOU'RE WELCOME to spend the day with me," Falconer said as he finished breakfast. "Although I can't promise it will be very entertaining."

"Don't worry about that. The best way for me to learn about you is to observe you going about your usual activities. Just forget I'm here."

He paused. "That will be rather difficult, but I'll try." Rising, he added, "Let's get started, then."

It was Tyne's turn to hesitate. She was only too aware that he was still dressed in his bathrobe and trunks, and she doubted very much that he intended to work that way. "I could meet you in your office."

He shot her a chiding look. "I don't like to waste time."

Tyne sighed, suspecting she was going to have to go along with him, but not without protest. "You really are very domineering, you know."

"Yes." He nodded. "It's one of my more endearing traits."

"If that's endearing, I'd hate to see what you consider offensive."

"Keep this up, and you may yet. Coming?"

"Sure, why not? I always interview men in their bedrooms."

His expression softened as she stood up, his eyes running over her caressingly. "Somehow I doubt that, but never mind. I'll be on my best behavior."

Tyne didn't believe him for a moment, but she wasn't about to admit it. Whatever Falconer Darcourt could dish out, she could hand right back.

He wouldn't get the better of her, nor would she let him weasel out of the interview.

"Shall we begin?" she said when they reached his bedroom. As she sat down at the table where he'd been working the day before, he disappeared through an open door, apparently to his dressing room.

Over the sound of running water, he asked, "What do you want to know?"

"For starters, where were you born?"

"In a hospital."

"Cute. I thought you didn't like wasting time."

He laughed gently and relented. "I was born in New York. My parents lived there for a brief time after their marriage."

"Why brief? Didn't they like the city?"

"They didn't like each other," he corrected quietly. "They were divorced when I was about a year old."

"So you were raised by your mother?"

"No." He hesitated for a moment, then added, "She became enamored of a hirsute young artist and ran off with him to the south of France."

"Your father raised you alone?"

There was a short, hard laugh. "Not exactly. I had two official stepmothers and a succession of unofficial ones before I was eighteen."

"Oh..." Tyne stared at her blank note pad, wondering why she wasn't jotting all this down. Though Falconer showed little bitterness about his upbringing, her cursedly vivid imagination filled in the details. A little boy abandoned by his mother before he was even old enough to know her, left to the tender mercies of a father far more concerned with other matters.

None of that was really relevant to her article, anyway, she told herself, and of only passing interest to Argus. Determinedly she moved on. "Were you being groomed to take over your father's business before he died?"

"What's that?"

"Did you always want a career in business?"

"I don't like this hollering back and forth. Come in here."

Tyne hesitated. She had been afraid this would happen.

Part of her was tempted to refuse and leave his suite; the other insisted she stop acting like a ninny. It was ridiculous to think that after all she had been through in life, she would quail at the thought of being close to a man in his bathroom. Yet the feelings he aroused made her anxious, despite her best efforts to deny that.

Professional pride demanded she stifle her concerns and get on with it. Cautiously approaching the open door, she peered around it.

Falconer stood at a black onyx sink that matched the huge sunken tub and double shower. He wore only a towel wrapped around his waist. His back was to her as he shaved.

"Sit down," he said, gesturing to a padded leather bench along one side of the vast bathroom.

Hastily she obeyed, noting as she did that a door on the other side led to what seemed to be a gym, while another gave way to a passage lined with fitted closets and cabinets. The entire area couldn't have been more masculine, and it reeked of luxury without ostentation.

Self-consciously crossing one leg over the other, Tyne tried to get comfortable. When that failed, she put both feet back on the floor and gripped her pencil more tightly.

From across the room, Falconer chuckled softly. "Relax. I don't bite, at least not under these circumstances."

Tyne met his eyes in the mirror and glared. "You seem to be enjoying making me feel ill at ease."

His mouth tightened at that accusation, at least in part because it was true. He wiped off the remainder of the shaving soap and turned to face her. "You're not very at ease around men, are you?"

Her face was deliberately expressionless as she studied the wall beside his head. "I never had any brothers to get me used to half-naked males wandering around the house."

His expression softened slightly. "What about sisters?"

"I was an only child."

"So was I. There's another thing we have in common."

Tyne wasn't so foolish as to ask what else they shared. She knew perfectly well that he was referring to their extraordinary physical response to each other, and she refused to comment on that. Especially not under such intimate circumstances.

"When I was doing my research for this story," she said, "I found very little information on the origins of Falcon Enterprises. It seems to have been extremely successful from the beginning, and to have expanded rapidly."

"That's true." Falconer opened one of the large closets fitted into a nearby wall and selected a pair of slacks and a shirt.

She held her breath, preparing to be nonchalant about whatever happened next, then let it go with a tiny sigh as he stepped into the dressing room carrying the clothes.

"We're involved in everything from energy resources to the production of metals and chemicals, shipping, textiles, grain and quite a bit else."

She heard the rasp of a zipper as he added, "I can get you a list, if you like. I have one somewhere."

"That . . . uh . . . would be nice."

He emerged from the dressing room still buttoning his shirt. His skin glowed with health and vigor. Tawny curls damp from his recent swim clung to his head. Several fell over his brow, making him look like a slightly rumpled lion fresh from its bath.

His clothes were casual, unbleached linen trousers and a cotton shirt, but perfectly tailored. He wore them with the ease of a man not particularly concerned about his appearance.

'I'll need that list,'' Tyne murmured, determined to stick to business, ''if I'm going to keep this all straight.''

''Fine—in the meantime, there's something else I want you to see. A side of Falcon Enterprises not very many people know about.''

Had he offered to show her a collection of dead, dusty butterflies, Tyne would have agreed. As it was, she eagerly accompanied him along the stone corridor that ran beside both their quarters, then down the curving staircase to the main floor.

Along the way he provided, at her request, a few details about his art collection. ''It started by accident about ten years ago when I was in Europe on business. I was buying the majority share of a large vineyard.''

Tyne already knew which one, but she asked nonetheless. When he named it she looked appropriately impressed, which wasn't hard to do, considering he was involved in the creation of what was regarded as one of the greatest wines in the world.

''At any rate—'' they passed through the iron-studded doors guarding the entrance hall and proceeded across the cobblestone courtyard and over the moat ''—the man I was dealing with had a magnificent collection of Renaissance art. He got me interested, but suggested I look around to see what period suited me best."

A self-deprecating smile lit his eyes. "I suppose the rest was predictable, considering how many times I've read the tales of King Arthur and his knights."

"Was that really what led you to the medieval period?" Tyne asked. "A fondness for romantic legend?"

"What better? Romance and art are inexorably linked. Both draw on a greater vision of what humanity can be."

"Not all art is romantic, surely. And besides, to call something romantic is often to belittle it."

"I've never understood why that should be the case," Falconer said. "Many contemporary artists and writers seem determined to wallow in the saddest, most dehumanizing aspects of our culture. They take an almost perverse pleasure in insisting that all human existence leads inevitably to misery. Whenever someone tries to look beyond that, to envision a better world, that person is called a dreamer or—if you will—a romantic."

They had reached the far side of the courtyard, arriving at the gate Tyne had been driven through two nights before. A security guard nodded respectfully as he hastened to open it for them.

The road on the other side was slightly uneven. She stumbled a bit, only to be quickly steadied as Falconer grasped her arm.

His touch, light though it was, sent a shock reverberating through her, the effect magnified by surprise at her own susceptibility. She stiffened and would have drawn away had he not instantly released her.

The sudden darkness of his eyes made her aware that she wasn't the only one startled. Spurred by some impulse she didn't fully understand, she asked softly, "Is that what you are, Falconer, a dreamer?"

They turned off onto a narrower path leading along the north side of the castle. "Sometimes. . . ."

"But how can you be? It takes hardheaded pragmatism to be as successful in business as you are."

He winced good-naturedly. "I suppose that's generally true, but not always. I have an excellent staff of pragmatists working for me. They run the day-to-day business of the company, while I'm left free to . . . dream."

"You must have had some degree of practicality, at least when you were starting out."

He shrugged lightly. "Like most people, I have several different, seemingly contradictory traits." As they rounded a corner he added, "You're a good example of that."

Startled and wary, she said the first thing that popped into her head. "Me? I'm just a simple little writer."

"And the earth is flat. You're forgetting that I've read your work."

"It's amazing what a good editor can accomplish."

He stopped suddenly and turned to look at her. "Why do you disparage what you do? I can't believe for a moment that you don't really know the worth of it."

She sought shelter in equivocation. "Haven't you ever heard that modesty is a virtue?"

"Ah . . . virtue." He spoke in a low, rolling tone. "Don't get me started on that."

"Why," she teased, appreciating his willingness to be sidetracked. "Are you lacking in it?"

He shrugged and started walking again, moderating his stride so that she could keep up with him on the steep, grassy slope they were descending. "That's for you to find out."

"Yes . . . I guess it is. By the way, where are we going?"

"I was wondering when you would ask. Most women insist on knowing such things right off the bat."

"Most? That sounds like stereotyping."

"My apologies. I'll rephrase. In my opinion, members of your sex show a commendable disinclination to follow along docilely without at least some indication of where they are going."

"Is that what you think I'm being, docile?"

He shook his head so quickly that she laughed. "No, that's one mistake I would never make. There is nothing in the least docile about you."

"Thank you," she said gravely. "So what do you think accounts for my being so, shall we say, pliant?"

"I think you're smart enough to know that by keeping silent and seeing what develops, you

can learn more than by demanding explana-
tions."

Since quiet watchfulness was precisely the
technique she had always used to get information, Tyne was taken aback. If he could really
see through her so easily, she might be in serious trouble.

"Are you always so perceptive?"

"No," he admitted, "but I have always been
rather interested in writers, how they manage
to sift through the overload of information that
surrounds us all to get to a few kernels of truth.
It's a fascinating process."

"Not to everyone," she murmured under her
breath. "Most people aren't even aware that it
goes on."

They had reached the top of a hill, which
offered an excellent view of the surrounding
countryside. Struck by the absence of all signs
of human habitation, except in the immediate
vicinity of the castle, Tyne asked, "Just how big
is your estate?"

"Five hundred acres," Falconer said with no
particular emphasis. "The castle and environs
have a total population of about four hundred
people. That includes some fifty members of the
household staff and the security force that fluc-
tuates, depending on need. The rest work at the
various installations I sponsor here."

Gesturing to the bottom of the hill, he said,
"That's one of them."

Tyne followed the direction of his hand to an
open area beside the river, where half a dozen
large greenhouses glistened in the morning sun.

Tools, sacks of dirt, coils of hose were scattered around them. A Jeep and several trucks were parked nearby. White-coated men and women could be seen through the glazed panels of glass, going about their duties with precision.

"What is this?" Tyne asked as she took in the pervasive sense of order and purpose.

Initially it had occurred to her that Falconer simply had a fondness for fresh flowers and vegetables, and the means to indulge his tastes. But she soon dismissed that explanation. There was an unmistakable air of professionalism about the place.

"It's an experimental botany station. Falcon Enterprises provides the funding, and some of our subsidiaries may eventually benefit from discoveries made here. But the primary objective is to find quicker, cheaper ways of growing food."

He opened the door to the nearest greenhouse and stood aside to let her enter. Damp warmth and the smell of moist, fecund earth enveloped them. It was very quiet inside; there were no sounds except the drone of the ventilator fans and the splash of water out of irrigation hoses.

On either side of the greenhouse, and in a row down the middle, plants grew in riotous abundance. Tyne tried to put names to a few, stopping when she realized that what she was looking at might well have no name, at least not yet.

Something that might have started as a corn plant grew close to the soil almost like a vine,

except for the large ears of corn fanning from
it.

Nearby, golden wheat grew downward from
baskets dangling from the ceiling. Lettuce heads
sprouted from holes poked in a fiber-board
wall. Bright red tomatoes blossomed from a
leafless plant that twined upward along a pole,
easily reaching twelve feet in height.

"What we're doing here," Falconer explained, "is trying to adapt high-producing
plants for different types of environments. Take
the wheat, for instance. There are places where
it just won't grow because the soil isn't right. So
we're developing a strain that doesn't need soil.
Its roots draw nitrogen directly from the air."

"That means it wouldn't be susceptible to
droughts or floods or any of the other problems
that can destroy a crop?"

"Exactly, so people who currently live in
the shadow of famine from harvest to harvest
would be able to escape that fear." He gently
touched a strand of the golden grain. "Of
course, practical use of this is still years off, but
at least we've made a beginning."

"Yes, I can see that," Tyne murmured, her
gaze going to the fish ponds supporting high,
wide trellises of beans and other legumes that
flourished on the fertilizer provided by the sea
creatures.

There was also a special area set aside for a
happy colony of rabbits, whose high body tem-
peratures provided the heat needed by plants—
specially bred to be unappetizing to their bene-
factors, of course.

Most remarkable, to Tyne at least, was the family of pigs that lived contentedly on waste from the plants while obligingly producing methane gas, which in turn fueled the ventilator fans and water pumps.

"As you can see," Falconer said, "everything here is intended to operate on a small scale, in a village, for instance, or among a group of families. That's how things happen in the Third World. Any attempt to impose large-scale technology is bound to fail."

"So you tailor the technology to the culture."

"Exactly." He smiled warmly, obviously pleased by her ready understanding. "This is not in keeping with the scope of most Falcon Enterprises projects, but it is effective, and that's what counts."

On the basis of the evidence in front of her, he seemed to be correct. The systems being devised under his patronage did work. But when Tyne thought about their ultimate objective, she strongly doubted their chance of success.

Falconer was attempting to help feed the roughly one billion people who routinely went to bed hungry every night. That was a task she doubted any man could accomplish, even one so powerful. Only a dreamer would try.

"Are there other projects like this?" she asked as they left the greenhouse.

"Several, mostly having to do with alternate energy sources." He grinned engagingly. "We've got a terrific windmill on the other side of the castle."

"Could I see it?"

"Sure." His quick response made it clear that he wanted to show it to her, yet he hesitated before adding, "We don't have to do it today, if you'd rather not. I know this kind of stuff tends to bore people."

"Not me," Tyne told him truthfully. She might think he was wasting his time on an idealistic mission, but she was still interested in seeing how he was going about it. "I think it's fascinating. Besides," she went on after a moment, "it will give a whole new slant to my article."

"Oh, yes, the article..." Falconer wondered how he had managed to forget about that. In the past few minutes, talking with her and seeing her quick appreciation of what he was trying to achieve, he had lost sight of the reason she was there.

They began walking in the direction of the windmill, chatting along the way about Falcon Enterprises. "How did you get the original seed money to start the company?"

"I... came into some funds about fifteen years ago and used them to start the business."

"Are you saying you inherited money?"

He laughed softly. "No, there was nothing left to inherit. I earned the capital that set up Falcon Enterprises."

She frowned, asking herself how a young man of twenty-three, as he would have been then, could have made so much money. "That's very impressive," she said cautiously. "What kind of work were you in?"

"Whatever I could get. After my father died

Discover a world of romance and intrigue in days gone by with 2 Masquerade historical romances FREE.

Dear Susan,

Your special introductory offer of 2 free books is too good to miss. I understand they are mine to keep with the free necklace.

Please also reserve a Reader Service Subscription for me. If I decide to subscribe, I shall receive four brand new Masquerade romances every other month for just £6.00 post and packing free. If I decide not to subscribe, I shall write to you within 10 days. The free books are mine to keep in any case.

I understand that I may cancel my subscription at any time by writing to you. I am over 18 years of age.

5A6M

Name _____ Signature _____
(BLOCK CAPITALS PLEASE)
Address _____

_____

_____ Postcode _____

To Susan Welland
Reader Service
FREEPOST
P.O. Box 236
CROYDON
Surrey CR9 9EL

NO STAMP NEEDED

SEND NO MONEY NOW

and I realized I wouldn't be able to hold on to the company, I had a succession of odd jobs." He grimaced. "Some more odd than others. At any rate, in my early twenties I ended up in South America, working with a construction team in Brazil. There was a gold rush under way, so I joined it." His eyes darkened at the memory.

"That's the hardest work I've ever done in my life. Down in a pit day after day, digging tons of dirt with no more sophisticated equipment than a pick and shovel. Most of the prospectors never made a penny, but I got lucky. I hit a strain of pure gold nuggets, some so large I could barely hold them in two hands. Within a month, I had millions of dollars."

Tyne listened to his story with growing astonishment. What he was describing was the stuff of legend, or fantasy. Yet he had actually struck it rich. "How did you feel when you realized what you had accomplished?"

"Actually—" he shrugged lightly "—I didn't think about it very much. All I could concentrate on was the need to make the most of my luck. I came back to the States immediately and began building up my operation."

"Did you begin with the intention of growing into such a powerful conglomerate?" Tyne asked.

"Not really. I never did much planning at the outset. I was too busy making the most of the opportunities all around me." He chuckled. "I now have a very expensive staff that does nothing but plan what Falcon Enterprises' next moves should be. Sometimes the strategies they come up with make sense, and sometimes they don't. I still rely pretty heavily on instinct."

"You don't sound very concerned about that."

"Well, part of the joy of life is the surprises it throws. I wouldn't try to do away with that for the world." Turning to look at her, he said, "For example, I certainly couldn't have predicted how I would react to you."

Tyne flushed, finding the teasing gleam in his eyes disconcerting. She didn't want to be reminded of that first scene in his bedroom. "It works both ways," she pointed out quietly. "You've come as quite a surprise to me."

He liked the candor of that. It took courage to be so honest. "How do you feel about surprises in general?" he asked with seeming casualness.

"They . . . unsettle me."

"Why do you say that?"

"I suppose because I'm a very orderly person. I like to know what's what. Everything in its place and a place for everything." She laughed uncomfortably. "I must sound very dull."

"No," he assured her, "though I have to wonder how you got that way. For a writer, the desire to impose order can be both a blessing and a curse. It's necessary to the creative process, but taken too far it can destroy inspiration."

"I disagree. There's nothing wrong with order," she insisted. "It's the people who let themselves drift, who go along with their heads full of dreams, imagining that the world is better than it is, who end up in trouble."

Falconer looked at her intently. He heard the pained note in her voice and suspected that her disillusionment sprang from hard experience. Whatever the actual details, she had been through something that had left her wary and disinclined to trust in dreams.

Which meant that it would be all the more difficult to woo her to him. But not impossible. He was, after all, a man of patience, well schooled in that subtle art, much like the hunter stalking his prey.

Not a very pleasant simile, he admitted, but apt nonetheless. A hunter pursued what was essential to life. He was beginning to suspect that in this case he was doing the same.

ONLY MUCH LATER in the day, as he was at work in his office, did it occur to Falconer that Tyne had deliberately turned their conversation away from talk of her family life and focused it on his professional background.

He frowned slightly. Had she done so merely because as a reporter she was accustomed to asking questions rather than answering them? Or was there some other motive? Was he wrong to suspect she was unusually reluctant to give any information about herself?

He grinned wryly at his own concerns. Before much longer he'd be like Winston, spotting shadows in every corner. The security chief had even seen fit to mention that, according to the guard's log, Tyne had slept well during her night in the cell. He seemed to think that unusual.

Falconer's smile faded. He remembered then that Tyne hadn't corrected him the next day when he had suggested she must be tired. On the contrary, she had allowed him to believe that was true.

Why?

He stared out through the windows to the garden, wondering about the significance of something so seemingly inconsequential.

7

TYNE GAZED into the green phosphorescent screen of her portable computer, trying to get her thoughts in some sort of order. She had spent the morning transcribing the notes collected over the past few days. During that time, she had learned a great deal about Falconer's many and varied businesses, as well as a fair amount about the man himself.

He was complex, fascinating, exciting, puzzling ... there were all sorts of ways she could describe him. In his outlook and behavior he seemed to stand on the cusp of the medieval world and the Renaissance, a time of explosive energy and discovery whose echoes were still being felt. Yet he was also undeniably a man of the future, concerned with the fate of the world and the people in it.

Given all that, she really wasn't surprised to be making such little headway with her profile. With a soft sigh she leaned back in her chair and let her mind drift over the past few days.

Just as she had intended, they had been together almost constantly, from early morning when she joined him at the pool to late in the evening when they lingered over after-dinner brandy. They talked about many things, but

rarely touched on personal subjects. She was
wary of letting down her guard too much with
him, and he was too wise to press her.

But each day, each hour they spent together
brought them closer.

Tyne looked away from the flickering screen,
staring out at the rolling green valley as a memory of the previous evening taunted her. With
the benefit of hindsight, she could see that, inevitably, she had violated her rule about becoming personally involved while on a mission.
Falconer had tempted her from the first; getting
to know him better had only intensified her unwilling desire. Last night she had come very
close to forgetting everything else.

They were playing chess. It was his idea; he
loved the game and asked if she had ever tried
it.

"Occasionally," Tyne allowed.

"Then you know the rules?"

Their eyes met over the snifters of brandy.
"Well enough," she said dryly.

Falconer gestured to the board set up on a
small inlaid table. "Perhaps you'd care to give
me a game."

Why not, Tyne thought. Playing chess with
someone was a good way of getting to know
how his mind worked. She agreed readily.

Seated across from each other, with flames
dancing in the marble-mantled fireplace and
Mozart on the stereo hidden away in the clois-
onné cabinet, they presented a very decorous
tableau. At first.

The opening moves of the game were both

simple and classic. Falconer advanced his knights; Tyne countered with her bishops. She took the precaution of castling her king early on, placing that vital piece in a protected corner of the board guarded by the castle towers called rooks.

Falconer had smiled at that. "You did warn me you don't like surprises."

"I prefer caution," she said, shrugging her lightly clad shoulders. Her black silk dress was almost austere in its simplicity. The square neckline barely hinted at the curve of her breasts, while the slender sleeves, plain waistline and straight skirt didn't distract from the pure lines of the body they covered. The drama of the dress came in what it did not cover: glimpses of alabaster skin and the unruly tumble of titian curls gleaming in the firelight.

Falconer's appreciative scrutiny assured his distraction, which evened the odds a bit, since she was equally aware of him. More casually dressed than on the evening of the diplomatic dinner, he was nonetheless compellingly attractive. The white knit turtleneck he wore beneath his dark-blue jacket emphasized his tan and the breadth of his shoulders, while tailored gray slacks did nothing to conceal the sleek trimness of his hips or the power of his long legs.

At midgame, as Tyne began to sense the flow of his strategy, she moved her queen into combat. The most powerful piece on the board, the queen could move almost at will. Some players were tempted to rely on that too heavily. The key to successful use of the sovereign lay in protecting her adequately.

Falconer's eyes narrowed slightly when he saw what she was doing. He moved out to challenge, and for a while the match seemed even. Each lost a knight and a bishop. Several pawns went down to defeat.

"You play better than I expected," he admitted.

She smiled faintly. "It's always a mistake to underestimate an opponent."

"Especially when it gives that opponent an advantage," he added wryly.

Her tapered fingers shifted her queen into position to take his remaining knight. As she placed the captured piece on the side of the board, she said, "Check."

Falconer looked startled. He studied the board for several moments. "I'm not quite sure how you did that."

"I'll be glad to show you, after the match. Or perhaps you would care to forfeit now?"

"I most certainly would not."

They played on as the flames danced and the music soared. Falconer was good; she had to admit that. Even handicapped by the loss of two important pieces, he gave her stiff competition. Had it not been for his original underestimating of her, she knew the game would have been much more even.

As it was, she still had a difficult time closing the trap around his king that would lead to the end of the game. He seemed able to anticipate her moves to a disconcerting extent and foiled many of them. But not all.

Quietly yet with unmistakable satisfaction, she continued the attack. With his king under direct challenge, Falconer had no choice but to respond defensively. He made several excellent moves to evade capture, but in the end could not. The gleam of victory was in Tyne's eyes as she struck the final blow with her queen. "Checkmate."

He sat back and stared at the board, his eyes flicking over it as though intent on absorbing every nuance of what had happened there. Slowly he said, "Do you know, this is the first time I've lost in several years."

"It's good for your soul," Tyne assured him. She was unabashedly proud of her win, especially since she knew it hadn't been easy.

"Hmm . . . maybe . . . but I could do with a little consolation." Reaching out across the small table, he caught her hand gently in his. "Shouldn't a gracious lady succor a vanquished opponent?"

Tyne's breath caught in her throat. The warmth of his fingers curling around hers set off sensations she didn't want to confront. But it appeared she had no choice, for she couldn't summon the will to refuse him.

He really was very tall, she realized dimly as he stood up and drew her to him. His shoulders were so wide that they blocked out the fire. She was aware only of the power of his body and the hunger of her own.

When he had kissed her that first day in his

bedroom, he had been unexpectedly gentle. This time was different. The pressure that had been building between them ever since then demanded release. His arms were bands of steel holding her, his chest the hard wall against which she lay unresistingly. As he claimed her mouth with devastating thoroughness, her passion matched his own.

The taste, touch and scent of him enthralled her. Impulsively she gently bit the tip of his marauding tongue, then sucked on it to ease the tiny hurt.

Falconer groaned deep in his chest. His hand tangled in her hair, urging her head back to give him access to the delicate line of her throat. Tremors undulated through her as his teeth raked her softly, before his lips nestled into the hollow between her collarbones.

"You're so sweet..." he murmured huskily. "So warm and responsive. I need you, Tyne, more than I've ever needed anything."

Her breasts, crushed against his chest, were swollen with passion, the nipples taut and aching. Molten heat gathered at the junction of her thighs, intensified by the hard proof of his arousal pressing into her belly.

"Falconer..." she moaned, "please...I hurt inside...."

"So do I, angel," he whispered, sliding his hands down to cup her buttocks and squeeze them. "So do I."

But what to do about the pain? To share with him the heights of intimacy would be magnificent; Tyne didn't doubt that for a moment. She did doubt her ability to walk away from such an encounter unscathed. On the contrary, everything she knew about herself and everything she had learned about Falconer told her she stood on the edge of a precipice, beyond which could lie either exultant joy or terrible regret.

Should she take the chance? For a moment she was unbearably tempted. Only caution, ingrained since childhood, prompted her to hesitate. She had felt all along that she was in a dream. Eventually she would have to wake.

Falconer had seemed to understand her refusal; certainly he had taken it without rancor. But something in the way he had looked when he let her go implied that all she had done was win a brief reprieve. The issue was by no means settled.

Impatient at the direction of her thoughts, Tyne turned back to the computer and typed in a command to save the material she had recorded, then switched the machine off. Clearly she wasn't going to get much work done that day.

She shrugged resignedly. Since she couldn't make any progress with the article, she might as well explore.

It was very quiet in the hallway; the servants had long since finished their vacuuming and polishing and withdrawn to other parts of the castle. Far off in the distance she could make out muted sounds from the kitchens and beyond.

Through the slit windows set at intervals along the corridor, she could see gardeners hard at work tending to the flowering fruit trees, as well as pruning bushes and setting out pots of bright orange-and-yellow marigolds.

A servant nodded politely to her as she crossed the hall and headed outside. The day was brilliantly clear, not hot but with a sultry warmth heavy with the scents of honeysuckle and roses. Bees droned busily as she made her way across the courtyard.

She wasn't headed in any particular direction, being content to simply wander. At length she found herself near the entrance to Winston Elder's office, and was pleased to see the silver-haired security chief coming toward her.

"Good morning, Miss Saunders," he said, inclining his head with exactly the proper degree of acknowledgment and deference.

Thinking of the change a few days had made in his behavior toward her, she smiled engagingly. "I find myself at loose ends, Mr. Elder. Could you spare a few minutes?"

He hesitated only fractionally before nodding. "Of course. Mr. Darcourt has said you are to receive full cooperation from the staff."

Tyne hadn't been aware of that, though the instruction didn't surprise her. She had come to understand that Falconer was thorough in everything he did.

Seated in Winston's office, in the same gunmetal-gray chair she had occupied a few nights earlier, she said, "I'd like to talk with you about the security arrangements at the castle. No details, of course," she added hastily as he started to demur. "Just some idea of why they are considered necessary."

The security chief cleared his throat cautiously. "As I'm sure you are aware, Miss Saunders, we live in a dangerous world. A man of Mr. Darcourt's stature has to take certain precautions."

"Of course, but I'm surprised by the extent of your arrangement. Are armed guards, night-vision cameras and so on usual?"

"We have stepped up security because of his involvement with the Bahdai negotiations," he admitted. "There have been ... indications that extremist factions would like to prevent any military treaty between the United States and Bahdai because of the treaty's implications for the total situation in the Middle East."

Tyne was well aware of that; still, she was determined to play her role. Grimly, she asked, "Are you saying that Mr. Darcourt is in danger from terrorists?"

Winston leaned back against his desk and regarded her somberly. "Why should that surprise you? He's been highly instrumental in bringing about a new understanding between our country and Bahdai. If the negotiations conclude successfully, our prestige and influence in the Middle East will be greatly increased. There are people who would do anything to prevent that."

Anything at all. Including murder. "Is that why he's staying here at the castle?" she asked quietly. "So that you'll be better able to protect him?"

Winston shook his head glumly. "I only wish that were the case. Unfortunately, Mr. Darcourt isn't the sort of man to let his actions be affected by any concern for his personal safety. He's here right now simply because he chooses to be. I'm not sure how long that will continue."

"Surely you can convince him to stay?"

"You've spent enough time with him by now to understand something of what he's like," Winston countered. "Do you honestly believe he can be expected to hide behind stone walls because a gang of rabble-rousers wants to do him harm?

"On the contrary," he went on, answering his own question. "The more convinced he becomes that he is in danger, the more likely he will be to continue with his usual activities. He'll consider it a point of honor not to give in to fear and intimidation."

"But his life could be at stake," Tyne protested dutifully. She knew all about Falconer's refusal to follow the strictest security precautions. It was the one chink in his armor. "Surely something can be done?"

"I'm not at all averse to getting some help with this matter, Miss Saunders. If you can convince Mr. Darcourt to show more regard for his own well-being, you will have my most sincere thanks."

Tyne knew a challenge when she heard one. A short time later, as she was leaving the security chief's office, she promised Winston that she would do her best to convince Falconer to stick close to home.

But as she spoke she doubted that even a genuine appeal would sway him. Her every instinct told her he wasn't a man easily influenced by anything save his own will and determination.

When he had left her at her door after dinner the previous evening, they had arranged to meet for lunch on the terrace. It was still a little early to expect to find him there, so Tyne wandered toward the stables, intending to visit a pretty little mare she was making friends with.

The horse nickered as she saw Tyne coming and arched her neck to be stroked. Tyne laughed indulgently, thinking how long it had been since she'd had a chance to ride.

She was standing there in the sun-warmed stable, watching dust motes dance above the beds of golden straw, when the sudden sense of someone watching her made her turn swiftly, her hand automatically reaching inside her tweed blazer, where a shoulder holster held the small, deadly automatic.

Falconer lounged against the open door of the stall. His face was cast in shadow, and the casual posture of his body was equally unrevealing. She wasn't fooled, though. She knew he was staring at her intently.

Abruptly self-conscious, Tyne stepped away from the horse, at the same time dropping her hand. "I've been exploring."

He moved from the door into the rays of sunlight. The mare nickered once more and butted her head against him. He smiled and rubbed her nose gently. "You've made friends with Dancer."

Tyne nodded, meeting his eyes over the

horse's mane. "She's a beauty. Have you had her long?"

"She was born here. Sired by Thor out of Caprice."

"I didn't realize you kept a breeding stable."

He grinned wryly. "I don't. On occasion nature will have its way."

Despite herself, Tyne blushed. She averted her gaze and stared down the line of stalls to the barricade that separated the mares from the stallions. Sounds reached her from the other side: the thump of strong hooves against wood; the snort of powerful lungs; the rumble of large, agile bodies moving restlessly.

A shiver ran through her, of excitement far more than fear. Dancer shifted beneath her hand. "I suppose I should be getting back to the castle," she murmured, "if I'm going to work."

"I've been thinking about that. How would you like to take the afternoon off and go for a ride?"

Startled, she said the first thing that came to mind. "That would be wonderful!"

He laughed with pleasure, his eyes caressing her. "You sound like a little girl let out of school."

Perhaps, but she certainly didn't feel like a child. Not with Falconer beside her.

They left the stables with the picnic basket he had arranged for, leading Dancer and a stallion named Pegasus who was about the same age as the mare. Tyne put aside whatever doubts she had about being alone once more with Falconer to enjoy the beauty of the day.

He paused long enough to collect from the aviary the falcon he was raising. Slipping a leather hood over the magnificent bird's head to keep him calm, he said, "I found him when he was a fledgling. He'd fallen from the nest and broken a wing. That was six months ago. Since then he's healed well, but he still doesn't seem ready to go off on his own."

"When he does, will you let him go?" Tyne asked curiously. The bird perched on Falconer's arm, looking for all the world as though it belonged there.

"Of course. I don't keep hunting birds, mainly because I don't much like to hunt. But I am trying to reestablish endangered species in the wild. So this fellow will get his chance." He stroked the bird's golden breast. "I think it will be soon now."

Tyne nodded and turned her eyes away, not wanting to see the wistfulness in Falconer's eyes. He would miss the bird when it went, but he wouldn't for a moment try to deny it freedom.

Under a cerulean sky softened by wisps of pure white cloud, they trotted over the cobblestone courtyard, beneath the arching gate and along a path leading southward.

Bees hovered over large patches of honeysuckle clinging to rock outcrops. Trout leaped out of the crystalline lake below, returning with a splash that sent diamond droplets of water into the air. A deer paused high up on a ridge to watch their progress, alert but unafraid.

Tyne felt the tension easing out of her and

lifted her face to the sun. "It's been so long since I've ridden," she said, echoing her thoughts in the stable. "I'd almost forgotten how lovely it can be."

"Don't you get much opportunity in Connecticut?" His hands were light on the reins as he expertly controlled the high-spirited Pegasus.

"There are stables near where I live, but I always seem to be too busy. Besides, riding should be for the wide-open spaces and places that are still untouched."

"Not too many of them are left. That's one of the reasons I'm so careful about who comes onto this land. It's home to thousands of animals who need a sanctuary."

"And you provide that?"

"I try to. Hunting is kept to a minimum, just enough to protect the herds from starvation in winter. There's a wildlife veterinarian on duty year-round, and if the weather gets really rough, we make supply drops."

He shrugged philosophically. "Compared to the despoiling that's gone on, this isn't much, but at least it's a beginning. I'm setting up similar areas in Brazil and Canada. They'll give scientists an opportunity to study animals that might otherwise become extinct."

"Perhaps," Tyne ventured, "it isn't only the animals that need a place to be free."

Falconer cast her a swift, narrowed glance. The horses had come to a stop on a crest overlooking a waterfall. Ancient pine trees, tall enough to scrape the heavens, stood proudly.

Farther off, a forest of oak and maple drowsed in the sun.

It might have been a hidden world untouched since the dawn of creation. A place that many people would have found intimidating, and that they would have harmed. Yet Falconer was perfectly at home in this environment; only her question discomfited him.

He sighed. "Is that what you're going to put in your article, that I'm some kind of primitive man uncomfortable with what passes for modern civilization?"

The horror with which he obviously regarded that possibility made her laugh. Teasingly she said, "Hmm...that might not be a bad idea. Sort of a Tarzan of the Adirondacks. What do you think?"

"I think you have a perverse sense of humor that is likely to get you in trouble one of these days," he informed her succinctly.

"Only if provoked by silly questions. Although," she admitted, "I suppose some reporters would grab hold of an angle like that. It's the kind of thing that makes writing easier."

"You don't strike me as the sort of person who takes the easy way," he said as they guided the horses back onto the path and continued southward.

"You're being perceptive again," she murmured, almost to herself.

He laughed softly but didn't speak again until they had topped the crest and entered a field of wild grass and flowers, where a flock of long-horned goats was grazing. The animals darted

off at their approach, but didn't go far, returning to their meal after only a brief time.

"Do you come here often?"

He nodded and set the falcon on a nearby
branch. Having dismounted swiftly, he caught
her as she did the same. With her body cradled
against his, he murmured, "Yes, I do. It's a good
place to think."

Or to feel. The fabric of his shirt was cool and
slightly damp beneath her hands. He smelled of
wind-freshened air and ripe grass, pure soap
and sun-warmed skin. She could hear the rush
of her sharply inhaled breath mingling with the
far-off cry of heron nesting on the lake. Raw
strength emanated from him in dizzying waves,
made all the more forceful by the tight restraint
he was imposing on himself.

A heady sense of her own power as a woman
swept through her, prompting a smile of pure
temptation.

"Tyne . . ." he murmured raggedly, his hands
tightening on her upper arms. "I really only
planned to bring you out here so we could talk
without interruption."

"We've talked a lot in the past few days," she
reminded him, gazing up through the thick
fringe of her lashes at the cleft in the center
of his chin and wondering absently what he
would taste like there.

"Only about certain things," he insisted grimly. "There are still barriers between us."

Her eyes widened slightly, his honesty surprising her. Hadn't she been thinking the same thing

that morning? "It's true," she said. "There's still so much I don't know about you."

"Or I about you." Letting go of her, he stepped back slightly and smiled. "So before I forget about my good resolve, let's relax and get to know each other."

Beneath the lightness of his tone, she sensed a deeper urgency, and that he wasn't kidding when he suggested a struggle was going on inside him.

Knowing he wanted her pleased Tyne, but not as much as the realization that his interest went far beyond the drive for mere physical gratification.

The logical, orderly part of her mind told her she was crazy to even consider a personal relationship with him. Meanwhile the more romantic side, so long suppressed, was surging to the fore with a vengeance. It insisted that she would be a fool to throw away at least the chance of getting to know so fascinating a man.

And Tyne, whatever weaknesses she had, was not a fool.

"All right," she said quietly. "Let me help you get the horses settled, and then we'll talk."

8

THE HORSES WERE TETHERED a short distance away, contentedly munching at the grass. The picnic basket held only a few remnants of crisply fried chicken, and the sun was beginning to slant westward.

Leaning over to refill their wineglasses, Falconer prompted, "So after you graduated from college in New York, you started looking for a newspaper job."

"That's right." Tyne smiled as she spoke. With her stomach full and her head just the tiniest bit fuzzy, she could look back on that time with a detached fondness, almost as though it had really happened.

Part of it had, and it was on that she concentrated. "I lived in a tiny apartment on the West Side. *Not* the fashionable part, really cold-water-tenement stuff. And I worked at anything I could find, which wasn't much at first. It took me about six months to get my first article published, in a tiny weekly that specialized in hog-belly futures."

Falconer laughed as he gazed at her. "Were you always determined to do business reporting?"

"Yes...I was very attracted to the pragmatism of the business world." She had had to be, since Argus had decided that was the perfect cover for her other activities.

"Some people would call it ruthlessness," he pointed out.

"Oh, that exists all right. It's part of the real world. I've never had any illusions on that score."

"It sounds to me as though you allow yourself very few illusions, if any."

"What would be the point? I'd only end up disappointed."

"Perhaps, or perhaps you might discover that the world is better than you think." Leaning back, he surveyed her gently. "Tell me something, is there anything you would change in your life if you could?"

Tyne hesitated, then nodded slowly. "I wish I had been ... closer to my parents."

"Are they still alive?"

"No ... they died a long time ago." And the memory was still agonizing. She looked away, hoping he wouldn't see the pain in her eyes.

Falconer frowned. He could feel something emanating from her, something dark and cold, anguished. ... "Tyne ..." He reached out a hand to her. "Tell me what happened."

She stiffened at the mere thought. The horror was so deeply buried, had been for so long. To speak of it would be to strip herself bare.

"They died, that's all."

He was silent for a moment; then his hand tightened on hers. "No, it isn't. There's more ... something very bad."

Her head snapped up. "How do you know that?"

"I don't, not for sure. I just feel it."

Was that possible? Could he really be so attuned to her as to sense her most personal nightmares? Cautiously she said, "There was an ... accident. My parents were killed."

"How old were you then?"

"Five."

She had looked away again, out over the rolling meadow to where the horses grazed. Her expression was shuttered, but as he watched a jagged pulse leaped in her throat.

Quietly he said, "You saw it happen."

Shock washed the color from her face. She started to pull away. "You *do* know...."

"No, I told you—" his hold tightened on her "—I just feel." That was true; he had no special knowledge of her. But he wanted it, badly.

She was silent for a long time. He saw the struggle going on in her, wished he could help, knew he could not. Relief spread through him when at length she made her decision.

"I was there. In an airport. A bomb blew them up. And a lot of other people."

"You said an accident...."

Her mouth twisted grimly. "The wrong place at the wrong time. It was nothing ... personal."

Nothing personal. Just one of those many random acts of terrorism that routinely made the headlines. Some group—the politics never really mattered—struck out in violence, mowing down innocent people, shedding blood for no better reason than to pander to warped egos.

The ultimate obscenity, Falconer had always thought.

"My God..." he murmured. To think of a child witnessing such a thing. Thickly he asked, "You weren't hurt?"

The look she gave him through half-closed eyes was indecipherable. "Not physically. I was...upset." There was no reason to tell him the truth; for a full year she had made no sound except to scream. When she had finally stopped screaming, she had had to learn again how to walk, talk, dress herself. She had regressed to an infantile stage, formless clay to be molded.

"Were there relatives to take care of you?"

"There were...people. They did a good job." Perhaps too good. Argus had taken the terrified, screaming child and transformed her into a woman afraid of nothing. Except her most wistful dreams.

"That's why you're so cautious," Falconer said quietly. "You're afraid of being hurt again."

He had touched on what increasingly seemed to her to be the major problem in her life. Living in a world where dreams were dangerous robbed her of the possibility of true happiness. Her fingers closed so tightly around the stem of the wineglass that she was afraid it would snap. Still she couldn't let go. Slowly she said, "I'm not really afraid, only cautious."

He put his own glass down and reached out, gently unwinding her fingers one by one as he asked, "Did you ever try to really trust someone after your parents?"

Yes, Argus. Impersonal, all-knowing, all-seeing

Argus. She could hardly tell him that. "No, not really. There aren't all that many people who inspire trust."

"Yes . . ." Falconer said. "I've learned that, too." Looking at her directly, he said, "But it isn't foolish to let yourself hope. Without it, there's no point in anything."

"There's survival," she protested. "You seem to know a fair amount about that."

"I do," he agreed, "enough to realize that I need more. To be precise, I need you."

The stark admission of his desire startled her. Her breath tightened in her chest, making her voice low and slightly rough. "I don't want to talk about that—"

"Why not?" he demanded huskily.

"Because you scare me." Which was quite an admission for her. Fear, insecurity, doubt were all aspects of life she preferred not to acknowledge. With Falconer she had no choice. He made the careful defenses she had built over the years tremble and threaten to crack wide open.

A dry laugh drew her eyes to him. "I'm glad you said it first," he admitted. "The fact is you scare me, too."

Her surprise brought another chuckle. "Did you imagine I couldn't be frightened?" he asked gently. "I'll admit I can't remember the last time it happened, but that doesn't make me completely invulnerable. On the contrary. I seem to be even more susceptible than I would have thought possible."

"S-susceptible to what?" she mumbled, hardly daring to believe what she was hearing.

"To you, to the way you make me feel and the

things you make me think of. To genuinely
needing instead of just wanting . . . to the knowledge that I'm not truly complete within myself . . . to all sorts of difficult and dangerous
ideas I have managed to avoid all these years."

Tyne stared back at him intently, searching
his face for some sign of deception. When there
was none to be seen she shook her head dazedly.

"I can't take this in. Here I sit in a field far
away from everything else on earth, having
come from what seems like an enchanted castle,
with a man who could surely have just about
any woman he wanted, and he tells me I mean
something special to him. It's like a dream."

"And you don't believe in dreams?"

She shook her head sorrowfully.

Falconer stared at her for a moment. Then he
lay back and drew her to him. "Well, I do,
sweetheart. And I'm determined to prove to
you that they can come true. I'm also willing to
be patient." Smiling tenderly, he asked. "Will
you take a nap with me before we start back?"

"A-all right . . ." Tyne agreed shakily, not
wanting to think about how good it felt to lie in
his arms. Somehow his embrace seemed the
most natural thing in the world, and certainly
the most comforting. She settled against his
chest, his heartbeat lulling her to sleep.

Her last thought before drifting off was that it
would be very easy to fall in love with Falconer.

THAT THOUGHT LINGERED about an hour later. She
came awake slowly, unsure of where she was
and knowing only that she felt unusually rested

and refreshed. Stirring, she discovered that she was securely locked in a pair of powerful arms.

Abruptly she returned to full consciousness. A quick glance reassured her that Falconer was still asleep. Unwilling to disturb him, she remained in his arms and gave in to the impulse to study him more closely.

In sleep his features were relaxed, the often predatory eyes hidden and the firm mouth softened. A lock of tawny hair fell across his broad forehead, half concealing the lines etched there. Other lines bracketed his aquiline nose and arched in fine webs around his eyes.

He was not a young man, she realized with something akin to surprise, despite the fact that she had known his age. His unbridled energy made it difficult to remember he would be forty soon.

Although the years hadn't left his face unmarked, they had had little effect on his body. Even without her vivid memory of him at the pool, the cotton shirt and jeans would have revealed that he was in peak condition.

Carefully, not wanting to wake him and end the moment, she raised herself up and studied him even more closely. The slight stubble of a day's growth of beard showed along his lean cheeks. She remembered that he invariably excused himself before dinner, returning once again clean shaven.

The cleft in his chin drew her eyes. She hesitated, then reached out a finger and touched it lightly. His skin, warm and firm, was like deep gold velvet. By contrast, her own looked much paler.

Tyne took a breath, waiting to see if he would wake up. When he didn't she grew more daring, her finger tracing the chiseled line of his mouth, parted slightly in sleep.

Drawing courage from his continued oblivion, she went further, exploring the bridge of his nose with a featherlight caress, moving upward to carefully trace the line of thick, sun-dusted lashes against his high-boned cheeks, discovering the silk of his hair in a touch that surely could have felt like no more than the ruffle of a playful breeze.

The slight fuzziness from the wine was long since gone. All her senses were vividly, almost painfully alert. Beneath her thin shirt and bra, her nipples were hardening, and deep within her a wellspring of need began to overflow. The hard press of the gun disturbed her. She hesitated a moment before getting up silently. Without letting herself reconsider, she removed her jacket and holster and placed both in her saddlebag. Then she returned to Falconer.

Remembering what he had said about needing rather than simply wanting, she smiled wistfully. A few days ago she wouldn't have understood the difference, but now it was only too clear.

Desire was a simple, straightforward appetite, to be quickly satisfied, if not satiated. Need was far more complex. It might be fueled by sensual appetites, but that was merely the beginning. Other hungers, unresolved since her childhood, were definitely involved.

Her brow furrowed thoughtfully. She didn't want to need; it opened her up to terrible disappointment. She didn't seem to have any choice. The man lying so quietly next to her had seen to that.

And saw more, she realized with a start. Even as the thought occurred to her that he was too quiet beneath her ministrations, he opened his eyes and met hers with gentle insistence.

She tried to move away, and just as automatically he lifted his arms to close them around her. For an instant she feared he might have seen the gun. But apparently not.

Drawing her to him, he turned over so that she was nestled beneath his big, hard body, her back pressed into a soft bed of blanket on top of fresh grass.

"Don't you think," he breathed against her cheek, "that it's time to wake up?" Before she could respond, he smiled and lowered his head, his mouth touching hers. Their first kiss had held tenderness, their second hunger. This time there was the recognition of mutual need and the beginning of trust.

Trust, Tyne thought distantly as her lips parted beneath his, was new to her. From childhood she had learned not to give it lightly. Now Falconer was coaxing it from her, with long, gentle kisses that told of his own surrender even as they brought hers ever closer.

His body, so much larger than her own, loomed above her, yet she had no sense of confinement or danger.

He was careful to hold his weight off her, careful not to scratch her skin with his stubbled cheeks, careful even to go slowly and give her time to adjust to what was happening between them.

"Did you mind my watching you when you were asleep?" she murmured as his mouth left hers to trail down her throat, finding unerringly the sensitive pulse point at the base.

"No," he breathed huskily. "I watched you once, after the diplomatic dinner."

Deep in her mind the vision flickered of darkness and moonlight and the tall shape of a man. She had been feigning sleep then; now she was fully awake. But was she truly, or was this all more of the same dream, begun the instant she stepped into his domain?

Impressions flitted through her: how startlingly gentle he was, how good his skin smelled, how much she longed to take him into her. Her arms reached up across his broad back, drawing him nearer. Her legs shifted slightly to make a place for him between them. She moaned softly as his hands closed over her breasts, cupping them as he rubbed her nipples through the thin cloth of her shirt.

The slanting sun sent oblique rays of gold washing over them. The muted sounds of the horses merged with the whisper of wind in the tall grass and the distant splash of water in the lake below.

Sun, air, earth and water—all were simply facets of the primal forces gathering inside her.

Their clothes fell away, removed by eager hands, his and hers, fumbling a little here and there, eliciting shared smiles and laughter. Naked, she felt no shame, only an overwhelming

sense of rightness. In this time and place, with
this man, nothing could be wrong.

Falconer lowered her again onto the blanket,
his amber eyes drinking her in as his hands ca-
ressed and his mouth searched. Her nipples
learned the touch of his tongue, rough as a great
cat's might be, laving over them. Her navel was
bathed in his kisses, as was the satiny skin of
her abdomen and inner thighs.

His fingers found her hot and moist, stroked
her to even greater heights, probed gently to ex-
cite her more.

Beneath him Tyne writhed, wanting to return
the pleasure he was giving her, but getting little
chance as he swept her from pinnacle to pinnacle.

She moaned once in protest, and he stopped
long enough to smile down at her. "This time is
for you," he told her huskily. "Later we'll
share."

Entwined in tightening coils of passion, she
had no choice but to agree. A fine sheen of per-
spiration made her body glisten. Soft curls clung
to her damp forehead. Her hands clutched at his
shoulders, and her eyes opened wide as he
found her most sensitive point and subjected her
to a loving torment that didn't stop until shards
of exquisite pleasure had shattered inside her.

Gasping, she cried out his name, bringing
him to her with the taste of her still on his
mouth. They kissed devouringly, tongues inter-
lacing, her breasts crushed against the pelt of
hair covering his chest and her legs captured by
taut limbs.

But that wasn't enough. A dark, pulsating chasm had opened up within her, demanding to be filled. She strained toward him, her hips lifting as her thighs parted farther.

He moved then with consummate grace and gentleness, bringing them together slowly, letting her adjust to the size and strength of him.

·When he was nested deep inside her, he smiled down into her dazzled eyes and touched his mouth to hers, murmuring, "You're so lovely . . . so tight and warm and welcoming."

"You feel so good . . . so hard . . . reaching so far into me."

"Move with me, love," he groaned, sliding his hands under her to grasp her buttocks.

The motion of their bodies, flowing together in perfect unison, drove the pleasure they shared to near-intolerable heights. Tyne's breath came in ragged gasps, as did Falconer's.

The muscles of his shoulders and arms bunched beneath glistening skin. He waited . . . waited . . . waited . . . giving her everything, not content until her head dropped back and she cried out hoarsely as the world shattered once more.

Only then did he find release, find within her body a fulfillment more profound than any he had ever known.

Much later, when they had recovered enough to move, they dressed slowly, pausing for long kisses and caresses, smiling at each other with their eyes. Tyne felt utterly replete and at peace with the world. She could hardly believe the storm she had passed through, or the safe harbor in which she now found herself.

Darkness was gathering over the eastern hills as they rode back to the castle. A pale moon rose out of the lake, illuminating their path. They held hands across the short distance separating them, but did not speak. The moment was too precious, trembling with the promise inherent in all they had shared.

Tyne shivered a little, wondering again at the difference between dreams and reality, and at how love made everyone a hostage to fate.

9

THE NEXT FEW DAYS passed in a blur for Tyne. Never before had she experienced such complete happiness and contentment, lit by periods of incandescent ecstasy that revealed to her for the first time her own capacity for joy. Never before had she lived in a world that had nothing whatsoever to do with reality, and could be smashed at any moment.

Falconer took a break from his usual schedule to spend all his time with her. They roamed over the estate until she felt she was learning to know the land as well as the man who was rarely far from her side.

Nights were spent in exquisite lovemaking followed by quiet talk as they lay in each other's arms. In the security of his embrace, Tyne found the courage to mention what Winston had told her about the terrorists.

"It is a possibility that I may be a target," Falconer admitted matter-of-factly. "But there's really no clear evidence of that. Abdul and Hiram are in far more danger."

Tyne sat up anxiously, heedless of the sheet that fell away to bare her breasts. In the moonlight pouring in through the high windows of Falconer's bedroom, her skin glowed opalescently. His gaze was on the firmness of her nipples he had so lately tasted when she said, "But you can choose to protect yourself."

Slowly he raised his eyes to hers. "How?"

"By staying here. Winston ... says you may not."

"I hadn't realized my security chief was so garrulous," Falconer murmured dryly.

Despite herself Tyne smiled. "It's your own fault; you told him to be cooperative."

"Hmm, within limits. I should have realized that he'd see a chance to turn this situation to his own benefit."

She shook her head in gentle reprimand. "Winston only wants what's best for you." After a moment she added, "As do I."

"I know." He grimaced wryly. "But there are larger concerns. The treaty negotiations have entered the final phase. If they're successful, we may have taken a very important step toward eventual peace in the Middle East."

Tyne shut her eyes and forced herself to take a deep breath. She was struggling not to express the grimness of her thoughts. Finally she said, "Falconer, there has been war in that part of the world for decades, centuries even. The same people have been fighting each other for so many generations that they don't know any other way of life. Do you really believe it can ever end?"

"It has to," he said quietly. "Fighting can't go on forever. Either one side acquires overwhelming force and conquers the other, or both sides are destroyed, or ..."

"Or what? Those are the only alternatives."

"That isn't true; there's another. People can choose to live in peace with one another."

Tyne turned away from him, rolling over on her side. Her voice was muffled by the pillow. "That's a dream, Falconer. And you're a dreamer. Reality isn't made for happy endings."

He was silent for a long moment before he murmured, "That's the crux of the problem, isn't it? You persist in believing that I've turned my back on the real world and am trying to construct a different one in its place."

"Aren't you?" she demanded, turning again to face him. There was anger in her light blue eyes, a gathering storm of fury at such blind refusal to admit the merciless truth about the world. "You live in a medieval castle, you spend a good part of your time working on quixotic plans to solve hunger and other insurmountable problems, and you think you can help to bring peace to a land where bloodshed is a way of life."

Her cheeks were flushed, and her hands clenched the sheet. "Wake up, Falconer!" she pleaded. "You've been lucky this far, incredibly so, but your luck is bound to run out. Why risk that?"

"Because," he said very softly, "I believe in dreams. Without them, life isn't worthwhile."

Tyne opened her mouth to argue further and found she couldn't. His absolute calm insistence on pursuing a course that could lead him to disaster left her numb. She had no response except to try instinctively to pull away from him.

That Falconer would not allow. Even as she attempted to leave the bed, he drew her back, holding her firmly in his arms as silent sobs shook her slender body and tears coursed down her cheeks to wet his chest.

Tyne couldn't remember the last time she had cried. It hurt badly, but it was also a catharsis. Falconer soothed her, whispering words of love and reassurance until she fell into exhausted sleep.

IN THE MORNING she awoke to the panic-stricken realization that he was gone. Stretching her hand across the bed, she found it empty and sat up swiftly. The memory of the words they had exchanged the night before stung her. She should have been calmer, better able to reason with him. She had let her emotions overcome her.

Jumping from the bed, she picked up her robe from the floor and put it on quickly. Sounds from the courtyard below drew her attention, and she crossed hurriedly to the windows to peer out.

Archery targets had been set up along one side of the cobblestone enclosure. Winston and several of the security guards were standing some distance from them, but they weren't the ones who drew her attention. Fascinated, she stared at Falconer as he stood bare chested in the sun, the muscles and sinews of his torso knotted with the effort to bend a longbow even taller than him. The weapon looked as though it had been plucked directly from the Middle

Ages, when such tools of war demanded immense strength and skill.

Falconer clearly possessed both. As she watched, hardly daring to breathe, he slowly but unrelentingly drew the bow back until it arched so tautly that she thought it must surely break. His corded arms were absolutely steady as he took aim and shot, landing the arrow squarely in the center of the target some two hundred feet away.

Winston turned to him and grinned, saying something Tyne couldn't make out but that was evidently congratulatory. Falconer shrugged offhandedly. The two men went off together to another part of the courtyard, where several mats had been laid on the ground.

Tyne turned away from the window and hurried to get dressed. She needed to see Falconer, to speak with him, to be sure he didn't resent her concerns about his safety. But when she reached the yard, she discovered she would have to wait a little while for his attention.

During the days she had been at the castle, she had learned that all the security guards kept in peak condition through a rigorous program of exercise and martial-arts training. Evidently Falconer didn't exempt himself from that discipline.

Standing off to one side, hidden by the shadows of a stone overhang, she watched as he and Winston tested each other's skills with lightning-fast karate jabs that, given a single break in concentration, could have been deadly. She more than most was able to appreciate the level of expertise she was witnessing. While wondering how Falconer had acquired such skill, she marveled at it. Should he choose, she didn't doubt that he could destroy any opponent in unarmed combat.

When the practice was finally over, both men seemed in high spirits. They were laughing together when a steward arrived to tell Falconer he had an important overseas call. As he went off to take it, Tyne stepped from the shadows to confront Winston.

"What was all that about?" she demanded.

Wiping the sweat from his face, Winston shrugged. "You mean the judo? Falconer just felt like a little workout." As he spoke he cast her a swift glance that suggested she might be responsible for his employer's need for vigorous exercise.

"You've always called him Mr. Darcourt before," she reminded him quietly.

Winston's steely eyes locked on hers. "It's a formality I let drop occasionally."

"Why now?"

"Because . . . you're no longer a stranger."

Tyne exhaled slowly. She wrapped her arms around herself and shivered slightly. "I'm feeling like one."

The security chief's rugged features softened. Gesturing toward the door that led to his office, he said, "Care to have a cup of coffee and tell me about it?"

She smiled shakily. "I think that might be a good idea."

"Give me ten minutes to clean up."

Later, seated in Winston's office, she said, "I tried to talk with Falconer about the terrorists. As you anticipated, he refuses to let them influence his behavior."

"I'm sorry to hear that," the security chief said. As he poured coffee for them both, he went on, "But I can't say I'm surprised. Falconer has seen far too much of violence to give in to it at this stage."

"I realize he had a tough time after his father died, but..."

"Do you?" Winston set a cup before her. "Somehow I doubt he's told you everything."

"I know about Brazil and the gold mine...."

The security chief grinned. "Oh, yes, that's the good stuff. It will be a while before he opens up about the bad experiences."

"But he said mining gold was the toughest work he'd ever done."

"Physically, yes, but hardly emotionally or psychologically. He'd been through a much rougher time than that before he ever got to Brazil." Winston hesitated for a moment, as though debating how much to say. "Did he give you any hint of what he was doing between the time of his father's death and when he turned up in Brazil?" he asked quietly.

Tyne shook her head. "He said he had odd jobs, some odder than others."

Winston chuckled. "He would put it like that." Leaning forward, he looked at her closely. "Before I go on, I want to ask you something. How do you feel about Falconer?"

Taken aback, she hesitated. Truth was so

dangerous. "I-I care for him, of course. We've grown rather...close...."

"Is that all?"

She laughed nervously. "What do you want me to say? That I'm in love with him?"

"Yes," Winston said flatly. "He doesn't deserve anything less." At Tyne's startled look, he went on. "I suppose you think I'm out of line telling you that, but the fact is I owe Falconer. He saved my life fifteen years ago, under circumstances where just about any other man would have left me to die. We lost touch with each other for a while, but when he founded Falcon Enterprises he got hold of me and suggested I take this job. When I agreed, I knew I would do my damnedest to keep anything from hurting him."

The coffee suddenly tasted bitter in her mouth. She put the cup down. "I see...and you think I may do that."

"It's a distinct possibility. You've gotten to him in a way no one else ever has."

Even as those words spread a warm glow through her, Tyne tried to resist them. "Surely he's had many other relationships with women."

Winston shrugged dismissively. "He's a man, not a monk. None of them counted for anything. You do."

"Why are you so sure?" she asked shakily.

"Because he's let you see his dreams."

Tyne opened her mouth to speak and found she had nothing to say. She could hardly deny Winston's words any more than she could explain her own fears. Her lower lip trembled slightly when she finally asked, "Will you tell me what you started out to, how he learned to fight so well?"

Winston stared at her for a long moment before he shook his head. "Ask Falconer." More gently he added, "Perhaps then you'll understand why reality isn't too attractive to him."

Tyne meant to take that advice. She hoped that if she could get Falconer to tell her about the side of his life he had so far kept hidden, she might learn something useful to her mission.

But before she could do so, he dropped a bombshell that destroyed all her best intentions.

Barely had they sat down to dinner that night when he said, "I have to go to New York tomorrow. I'd like you to come with me."

Tyne took a deep breath and fought to still the sudden drumbeat of fear echoing through her. "W-why?"

He smiled very faintly. "Why which? Why do I have to go, or why do I want you to come with me?"

"You know what I mean. Why place yourself in danger?"

"Because a snag has developed in the treaty talks. Both Abdul and Hiram think I can help smooth it over, so they've asked me to come down."

"They could come here."

He shook his head. "They aren't the only ones involved. There are other men on both sides who don't know me as well. If I appear afraid to them, anything I say will be given very little weight."

"You're telling me that if you had a healthy—not to say sane—respect for your safety, they'd think you were somehow weak?"

"And they would be right. We can't let ourselves be controlled by threats."

She stared at him over the damask tablecloth set with exquisite china, crystal and silver. He looked determined and unshakable, a rock against which she could throw herself endlessly without effect.

Yet she sensed the impression was misleading. A flicker in his eyes suggested he hadn't asked her to come with him lightly. He truly needed her. That made him even more vulnerable.

Once she realized that, there was no decision to make. "Will I have time to pack in the morning," she asked, "or should I do it tonight?"

The quick look of relief Falconer shot Tyne told her he had actually thought she might stay behind. Some of her annoyance at his stubbornness faded, and she smiled. "You didn't really think I'd deny myself the pleasure of your company?"

"It had occurred to me," he admitted. "I know what you think of my dreams."

"Let's forget that for the moment," she murmured huskily. "You still haven't answered my question. Should I pack tonight or in the morning?"

"In the morning," he said, reaching out to

take her hand in his. His thumb rubbed against her palm evocatively. "You're going to be too busy tonight."

AND SO SHE HAD BEEN, Tyne reflected a bit groggily the next morning as the helicopter lifted off from the pad behind the castle and banked southward. Falconer's lovemaking had been fiercer and more demanding than ever before. A note of urgency had crept into their relationship. It had been close to dawn before he'd let her sleep, and only a few hours before she had to get up to prepare for the trip.

Glancing at him out of the corner of her eye, she saw that he was immersed in a stack of papers. They didn't prevent him from shooting her a hotly tender look that spoke volumes. Piqued by his silent challenge, she returned it in full, until he shook his head wryly and said, "I may be in no shape for the meeting, but I guess there are worse fates."

"I could go to Connecticut and check on my plants," she informed him promptly, then held her breath to see how he would answer.

"Absolutely not. You're supposed to be researching an article about me, and that being the case, I expect your undivided attention."

His flat insistence that she stay with him was very gratifying. At least it reassured her that what had passed between them might, against all odds, have a chance of surviving their return to the real world.

That return struck her forcibly as they landed at the heliport near the East River, where they were met by a limousine that carried them into midtown.

Staring at the crowded streets, Tyne was starkly reminded of why she had moved out of New York several years before. People flowed in ceaseless rivers, jousting with the cars that stumbled along bumper-to-bumper, horns blaring. The air was hot and saturated with the smells of exhaust, refuse and closely pressed humanity. Skyscrapers rising on all sides formed canyons cutting off the sky, making her wonder how she had ever existed—even briefly—in so claustrophobic a place.

In all honesty, she knew there were times when the city was beautiful: nights when the glimmer of millions of lights rivaled the heavens, days when a fresh breeze off the water was enough to put a spring in everyone's step and a tolerant smile on everyone's lips.

That wasn't the case just then. As they left the limousine in front of the hotel, she breathed a sigh of thanks for the refuge of Central Park directly across the avenue. It, at least, was an oasis reminding her of the sanctuary they had left behind.

Falconer's suite, kept exclusively for him despite the rarity of his visits, was a duplex high above the park. The first floor included an entry hall, kitchen, bath and living room, the latter complete with marble fireplace, grand piano and wraparound terrace.

Upstairs were three bedrooms, two of them part of a luxurious suite within a suite. Tyne found her bags in one of these and smiled at the thoughtfulness that kept Falconer from broadcasting their relationship even while ensuring she would be close at hand.

"Don't get too comfortable," he said sardonically as he came up to find her surveying her new surroundings. "I have every intention of convincing you to let me share your bed."

"I suppose that's fair," she acknowledged, going into his arms, "since I shared yours last night."

"Most delightfully, too, I might add." He cupped the back of her head gently as he spoke, holding her still for a long, slow kiss that ended only when Winston coughed discreetly.

"Excuse me, sir. You wanted to be reminded that the first meeting is in an hour."

When the slightly red-faced security chief had taken himself off, Tyne murmured, "Please be careful."

"I will be," he assured her gently. He opened the door that linked their rooms and was about to step through when he stopped suddenly. "Will you be here when I get back?"

"Of course. I'm going to drop by my favorite stores, then meet with my editor. I should be back well before dinner."

"I should have mentioned this sooner," he said, "but there's a party I ought to attend tonight. I'd like you to go with me."

"Just like a man," she teased. "Now I'll have to run around getting my hair done and searching for something to wear."

"Don't," he said quite sincerely. "Your hair is lovely, and from what I've seen, your wardrobe is impeccable. You'll be the most beautiful woman there.''

She was still savoring his compliments as she made her way to the lobby and got a cab to take her uptown. The West Side, the part written about in glossy magazines, was a mosaic of renovated brownstones, imaginative boutiques and exclusive restaurants. To Tyne, it had the air of an extremely elegant carnival, the sort of amusement park that might exist if all the world was upwardly mobile.

At a tiny shop crowded with barrels and bins, she purchased an assortment of scented soaps and bath oils guaranteed to make any woman feel luxuriously pampered. Farther down the block, she picked out a silk teddy so sheer as to make her blush. On the next corner, at a shop where she had bought the teal-blue knit, she found a concoction of a dress that perfectly suited her mood. Made of tiers of white lace alternating with black silk ruffles, the ankle-length dress had a gypsy look. A snug bodice hugged her breasts, and short sleeves revealed the slender lines of her arms.

It was a dress to dance in by firelight, to throw aside inhibitions in. A dress to make her revel in the sheer pleasure of being alive. A dress to wear for herself and for a special man.

The thought of how Falconer would react when he saw her in it made her brush aside his assurances that she didn't need to make any special effort for him. She paid the exorbitant price without flinching.

Seated in the back of a cab as it lurched its way downtown to the financial district, she smiled at her own pleasure in the shopping expedition and tried to sort through her thoughts before the meeting with her editor.

The offices of the *Financial Times* were in the nineteenth-century pile of stone near the corner of Wall Street and Pearl, not far from the famed Fraunces Tavern, where General Washington had said farewell to his troops. The marble lobby was cool and hushed, the elderly guard smiling as he recognized Tyne.

A bank of art-deco elevators led to the upper floors. She took one to the fifteenth floor, exiting into the crowded, hectic city room.

Several people waved as she made her way to the back corner, where Chauncey held court. He saw her coming through the glass partitions and rose to meet her.

"Good afternoon, my dear. You're looking lovely, as always. Here, let me help you with those bundles."

"Thanks. I didn't expect to do so much shopping, but I got a little carried away."

"All for a good cause, I'm sure," the tall, impeccably dressed man said. He saw her into a comfortable seat opposite his desk, then folded his lean frame into a leather chair and smiled benignly at her over the rim of his metal-framed glasses. "How's the story going?"

"Very well," she assured him promptly. "Mr. Darcourt is cooperating fully, and I expect the results to be well worthwhile."

"Hmm . . . any idea when you'll have something for me to read?"

Tyne hesitated. She wasn't about to hint to Chauncey, even indirectly, about the treaty negotiations. The outcome would inevitably shape her story, as well as provide another. Cautiously she said, "Soon, I hope. There's so much to learn. He's a fascinating man, and of course, no one has had such an opportunity before."

"My dear girl, I'm well aware of that, and I wouldn't dream of rushing you." His gray eyes narrowed a fraction. "It really is quite extraordinary that you made it into his lair at all, let alone were allowed to stay."

Tyne kept her expression absolutely deadpan. "You know what you've always said about being in the right place at the right time."

He grimaced slightly at having his own words parroted back at him. "Then you don't think it's at all surprising that he let you stay?"

The unmistakable hint of doubt in his tone made her shift uneasily in her chair. "Chauncey, why do I get the feeling you're sniffing around for something?" No sooner were the words out than she wondered if she'd been hasty. Talk about taking the bull by the horns!

He was silent for a moment, contemplating her. She met his gaze unflinchingly, praying she looked the picture of the earnest, sincere employee.

At length he sighed and smiled faintly. "I guess I am a little hyper about the Darcourt story. It will be quite a feather in all our caps, but beyond that, there have been certain rumors floating around lately . . ."

"There are always rumors about him."

"True, but not quite like what's going on now. Something about a huge deal of incredible importance. What have you heard about that?"

The question came so suddenly that Tyne had only an instant to steady herself. As calmly as she could, she said, "He's got several deals in the works now, all large and presumably important. There doesn't seem to be anything unusual about that. However, he is involved in several fascinating projects."

Swiftly she went on to regale Chauncey with details of Falconer's experimental botany station. He particularly liked the stories about the windmill and the rabbits and was soon chuckling.

"It seems there are depths to the man none of us has suspected. No wonder you don't want to rush the interview."

"I'm so glad you understand," she murmured, praying he couldn't sense her full relief.

"Hmm . . ." Those eyes were watching her again, taking in her flushed cheeks and the nervous twisting of her slender hands clasped in her lap. "I think I understand a great deal . . . or at least I'm beginning to."

Unexpectedly his gaze softened, a phenomenon Tyne hadn't previously witnessed; it only had the effect of making her more apprehensive.

Chauncey had a well-founded reputation for being dogged in the pursuit of a fact, any fact, under any circumstances. That was the essential reason for his rise to the editor's chair at the *Financial Times*, an ingredient he had never allowed himself to forget.

She sighed inwardly as the aquiline nose flared slightly, on the scent of something she had no doubt she wouldn't want to divulge. Their meeting, which she had hoped would conclude quickly and amicably, was growing more perilous by the minute.

Caught between the natural desire to be candid with him and the determination not to break faith with Falconer, Tyne knew no happy resolution was possible.

Until Chauncey showed an unexpected streak of charity. "Look, whatever is going on, I trust you to handle it properly. You're a professional, one of the best, and you've never let me down. You are also—" he paused, studying her once more "—a very beautiful woman, and I can't ignore the feeling that some cracks have developed in those well-defended walls of yours."

Oh, Lord, this was even worse than she'd feared. He not only suspected she wasn't being open about the story, he had guessed that her view of Falconer wasn't strictly objective.

If he believed she had compromised her integrity by becoming personally involved with a man she was supposed to be interviewing, he was capable of yanking her off the story no matter what the cost.

Chauncey, it seemed, had other ideas. Beneath that three-piece gray pin-striped suit and sinewy body, hidden under the shell of cynicism all good journalists instinctively adopted, beat the heart of a softie.

He shook his head, possibly at the folly of his own weakness, then said, "At least do me the favor of being careful. Some of these rumors swirling around about Darcourt say that he's in great danger. Apparently he's done something that has upset some very violent people. Cover the story, by all means, but please don't get in the way of any bullets."

Tyne clasped her hands more tightly in her lap. Quietly she asked, "Do you think the threats are really serious?"

Instead of answering directly, Chauncey tossed the question back at her. "Does he?"

"Would he be in New York if he did?"

"Maybe. He doesn't strike me as the sort of man who runs from danger."

"No, he isn't. He seems determined not to give in to what he regards as a bunch of overgrown bullies."

"Not a bad way to think of terrorists." Propping two well-shod feet on the edge of his desk, the editor tipped his chair back and stared up thoughtfully at the ceiling. "So big things are in the works, and Falconer is letting you stay close. Sounds as if I can look forward to more than the usual interview."

"Perhaps," she ventured cautiously, not wanting to tip her hand. "If nothing goes wrong...."

Chauncey straightened, eyeing her. "That's one good thing about being a reporter—even when everything goes wrong there's still a story in it."

She looked away, hoping he wouldn't see the pain that flashed across her face. It was a remorseless, journalistic truth that tragedy was often only so much grist for the news mill. Should Falconer be killed, the story would make headlines around the world.

She would be in the middle of it, expected to write the article that would undoubtedly put her way out in front of all her colleagues. Except that she would be utterly unable to write that story.

Standing up, she gathered her packages and headed for the door. Her hand was on the knob when she took a deep breath and said quietly, "I may need another writer to cover for me rather suddenly." She looked at Chauncey over her shoulder. "All right?"

He nodded somberly. "I'll be standing by." Gently he added, "If you need help, day or night, call me."

Tyne swallowed hard. She knew he was offering her far more than the professional assistance she would require if the story became abruptly, brutally personal. He was telling her he would be available as a friend at a time when she might need one desperately.

That meant a great deal to her, even as she prayed she wouldn't have to accept his offer.

TYNE HAD ONE MORE STOP TO MAKE before she was done, a tiny gallery in a row of brownstones on Madison Avenue. The gallery specialized in rare Chinese porcelains; even for that very exclusive neighborhood, the prices were extremely high and the management especially aloof. Few prospective customers wandered in twice.

A middle-aged man in a dark suit stood up as Tyne entered. He looked at her discouragingly. "We were about to close."

"I've come about the parrot."

"Mandarin dynasty?"

"No, Sung."

He nodded. "Ah, yes, I believe we may be able to help you. If you would care to leave your packages here . . ."

She did as he suggested, then followed him through a curtain to a back room. There he left her. Tyne waited until the curtain had stopped swaying behind him. When it had, she walked toward the far wall, stopping when she was close enough to reach a row of coat hooks attached to it. She pulled on the one farthest to the left.

A panel in the wall slid open. Beyond it was what appeared to be a small, bare closet. Tyne stepped into it; the panel slid shut again. A red light flicked on. From a speaker near the ceiling, a toneless voice said, "Identification?"

"Saunders, Tyne. Alpha 349."

A small box slid toward her at eye level. She leaned forward, placing her forehead against it. Inside, a camera scanned the intricate pattern of capillaries in her corneas. For each individual the pattern was unique, like fingerprints, only even more precise.

There was a moment's delay while the picture just taken was compared to that on file for her. When identification was confirmed, the far wall of the closet opened.

Tyne stepped through it, into the inner sanctum of Argus.

10

Tyne had been to many exotic places in her life, but never anywhere quite as extravagantly luxurious as the penthouse where the party was being held to honor Prince Abdul Shakir.

As the double doors opened to admit her and Falconer, she stared with unfeigned amazement at what could only be called an interior designer's dream—or nightmare. It was as though some whimsical genie had transported a sultan's palace to Fifth Avenue, complete with grim-faced guards, wafting incense and beautiful women.

These in particular caught her attention. Whereas she had been the only woman present at the last party she had attended with Falconer, here the ratio was distinctly lopsided in the other direction.

The two dozen or so men on hand were outnumbered by a choice selection of beauties intent on doing their best to please.

"Abdul has a rather wicked sense of humor," Falconer murmured as a rigorously expressionless butler accepted Tyne's white silk wrap. "He knows how Americans expect wealthy Arabs to behave, and he doesn't like to disappoint anyone."

"Hmm..." she murmured skeptically, shooting a sharp glance at a lissome redhead who wandered past, her eye unmistakably on Falconer. "How considerate of him."

"Just think of it as good, clean fun." Taking her hand, he added, "And remember who you'll be leaving with."

"You took the very words out of my mouth."

His possessive hand on her arm reassured her somewhat, as did the fact that he showed no inclination to leave her side over the next several hours.

The gypsy dress—the black and white ruffles a stark contrast to her titian hair—also helped her confidence, but she was still aware of the differences between her and every other woman at the party.

She alone was not gowned in a fabulous couturier creation and draped in precious gems. Her makeup was modest compared to some of the fantastic displays of "war paint" in evidence, and her hair, tumbling ingenuously around her shoulders, lacked the sleekness of high-priced styling.

At least it seemed that way to Tyne. What she counted as deficiencies others saw as assets. Falconer certainly did, and knew perfectly well that he wasn't alone. More than once he found it necessary to warn off another man with an icy stare.

Prince Abdul was an exception to this; he and Falconer liked and respected each other far too well for either to ever feel challenged by the other. The tall rapier-eyed prince joined them shortly after their arrival. He looked somewhat wearier than the last time Tyne had seen him, but nonetheless strong and resolute.

Taking her hand in his, he bent over it gallantly as he gave her an appreciative smile. "I see Falconer's luck is holding," he said. "My friend has informed me that you are as intelligent as you are beautiful, and that our secret is completely safe with you."

"Thank you," she murmured self-consciously. "I trust the negotiations are going well?"

"Better than we might have hoped, and I am optimistic that will continue." Casting a glance at his friend, he added, "At Falconer's suggestion, I have agreed with the secretary of state that you will be the first reporter to get the story when it breaks. In the meantime, let me say that we both appreciate your discretion."

She nodded again as they went on to speak of other things. The prince proved to be witty and engaging. Although he and Falconer both moved in circles generally far removed from her own, it turned out that her work had brought her into contact with many of their associates. She spent a pleasant half hour or so exchanging anecdotes.

Only gradually did Tyne realize their little group was the cynosure of all eyes, and why. She was monopolizing the attention of the two most powerful and attractive men in the room, a fact that wasn't making her particularly popular with the other guests.

A soft laugh rose in her throat as she had a sudden image of herself standing between the two tall, lean men, one with hair like beaten gold and tawny eyes, the other endowed with swarthy good looks few women could resist. They were in sharp contrast to each other, yet she sensed a shared strength of purpose and determination to succeed.

Her face colored slightly as she wondered exactly how much the prince knew about her relationship with Falconer. Did he wonder why his friend trusted her to keep silent, or did he understand that such faith sprang from intimacy?

Reluctantly she admitted to herself that Shakir was far too astute and experienced a man not to recognize what was happening between her and Falconer. Especially since Falconer was making no secret of it. He kept an arm around her waist, listened attentively to everything she said and rarely let his eyes wander from her.

If Falconer had been treating her simply as a new and indulged lover, she might have been better able to cope, even though she would have been hurt by such an attitude. But his tender attention, his obvious affection and admiration, even his ease with her, all made it clear she meant far more to him.

And that worried her. Had she been inclined to forget the shadow of violence hanging over them, the hour spent at Argus headquarters would have reminded her. She had come away knowing that the situation was reaching a critical point, and that she would probably have to take action very soon.

"Is something wrong?" Falconer asked quietly as he caught the sudden darkening of her eyes.

The prince had excused himself moments earlier to speak with a gentleman from the State Department, so they were briefly alone. Tyne took advantage of their privacy for a quick smile and a seductively murmured reply. "No, I was just wondering how much longer we'd be staying."

He raised an eyebrow teasingly. "Is the party boring you already?"

"I guess you could say I'm not good with crowds."

His grin warmed her all the way through. "That's fine with me. I prefer keeping you all to myself."

Pleased, she said lightly, "It sounds as though some of the Prince's attitudes toward women have rubbed off on you."

"Only recently," he admitted as he steered her toward the door.

"Can we really leave now?" she asked hopefully.

"I don't see why not. It was only necessary for me to make a token appearance. Besides," he added deliberately, "Abdul will understand." Her faint blush made him laugh.

Their progress was slow as many of the guests stopped them to have a few words with Falconer and cast curious glances at Tyne. He introduced her to everyone, was unfailingly polite, but did not linger.

The same expressionless butler handed her wrap to Falconer, who draped it over her shoulders. The security guards scrutinized the hallway as they stepped into it, then waited until the private elevator had opened for them before vanishing back into the penthouse.

In the sudden quiet following the din of the party, Tyne relaxed visibly. "I know a reporter is supposed to be good with people, and able to adjust to all sorts of circumstances. But I've never really learned to enjoy big bashes like that."

"Neither have I," he said as the doors slid open at the lobby.

Alerted by the guards upstairs, Winston met them there. He nodded courteously to Tyne, then said, "If you would wait here for just a moment...."

Falconer agreed, though he plainly chafed at the need for such measures. His impatience was evident during the couple of minutes it took to scan the street and ensure that both the limousine and the two security cars that followed and preceded it were in place.

Only then did Winston nod and open the outside door for them. As they stepped toward the limousine, Tyne caught a sudden movement out of the corner of her eye; automatically she stiffened, unobtrusively sliding her hand downward....

She had barely a split second to realize that a man had come out of the shadows near the apartment building's service door and was staggering toward them.

Winston's hand was moving to the holster inside his jacket and guards were sprinting toward them from the two other cars even as Falconer grasped Tyne's arms. Turning quickly, he put himself between her and the interloper.

The man stumbled against him, cursing mildly, his eyes half-closed and red-rimmed. " 'Scuse me, buddy. Yuh got a buck to spare?"

The man broke off, staring in as much surprise as his befuddled mind was capable of at the grim-faced security men suddenly surrounding him. "What'zit ... ? Hey, can't a guy even try t'make a livin' anymore?"

The stench of sour wine wafting from the man was the best claim for his genuineness, but Winston remained unconvinced. "If you'd get in the car—" he began, only to be cut off by Falconer.

"This fellow's no danger to anyone but himself," he said impatiently. "Let's get going."

The security chief nodded reluctantly and gestured to the other guards to stand down.

The wino, realizing he wasn't going to get a handout, launched into a tirade of self-pity combined with comments about the big shots who wouldn't give the little guy a break. He was still declaiming as the cars pulled away from the curb.

Seated in the back of the limousine beside Falconer, Tyne fought to control the coldness seeping through her. For an instant back there on the curb, she had come very close to blowing her cover. Even now, she wasn't sure the whole incident hadn't been a test. Administered by whom? Argus or Falconer or someone else altogether?

She listened mutely as Winston twisted in the front seat and said, "I'm very sorry about that. He must have been slouched down behind the doorway, so we didn't see him."

"It's okay," Falconer murmured, his arm going around Tyne's shoulders to pull her close. She relaxed slightly against him, struggling not to think of what might have happened.

"If you'll pardon my saying so," Winston went on, "this only points to the need for more stringent security."

At that, a low, bitter laugh broke from Tyne. Both men looked her way in surprise. "What it points to is the uselessness of such precautions. All it takes is a split second to kill someone, especially if the killer is willing to sacrifice himself."

"Don't think about it," Falconer said gently. He drew her head against his shoulder, stroking her hair as he shot Winston a quelling glance. "We'll talk about this some other time."

What good would that do, Tyne wondered numbly as the limousine sped toward the hotel. He wouldn't change his convictions, and she couldn't forget hers.

The limousine pulled into the underground garage of the hotel, and Falconer helped her from it. She was barely aware of the swift ride up in the elevator.

At the door to the suite, he said good-night to Winston and the guards who had kept watch during their absence. When they were at last alone, he turned to her and said gently, "I know that upset you, and I'm sorry you were exposed to it."

Tyne couldn't meet his eyes. "Let's forget it happened." Tilting her head in the direction of the bar, she asked, "Would you pour me a nightcap?"

He frowned slightly but nodded. "Of course. I'll join you."

She excused herself as he poured two snifters of brandy. She returned after the gun that accompanied her everywhere was safely hidden in her bedside table. He handed her a snifter, eyeing her carefully. It was unusual for Tyne to ask for a drink. Though she looked calm enough, he almost wished she would argue with him again about his safety. Her unnatural quiet worried him.

He was still thinking about that when she put down her brandy, though she had taken barely a sip, and crossed the small distance separating them. Falconer watched her, struck by the combination of exquisite beauty and almost desperate hunger.

"Tyne," he breathed huskily, "do you have any idea what it does to me to see you look like that?"

Her only answer, at first, was to brace her hands against his chest beneath the black velvet evening jacket and touch her mouth to his in a slow, languorous kiss that quickly sent the blood pounding through his veins. A single thought stood out in her mind: she wanted to recapture the essence of the dream they had shared at the castle, if only for one night.

With great concentration, no longer certain he could fully control himself, he set his brandy down and grasped her hips, urging her even closer.

"Show me," she murmured, her lips warm and moist against his. "Show me what I do to you." The tip of her tongue traced the ridge of his teeth, seeking the warm, moist intimacy of his mouth.

Falconer needed no further urging. His arms closed around her fiercely, the hardness of his arousal imprinted on the softness of her belly.

Her head fell back as their mouths sipped and tasted and consumed in a fiery prologue to the complete intimacy that couldn't be long delayed. Bending swiftly, he lifted her high into his arms and strode toward the spiral staircase leading to the second floor.

Her head rested against his shoulder as her hands tangled in his pelt of hair. The ruffled skirt of her dress rode up, exposing long, slender legs sheathed in sheer silk. A soft, throaty laugh bubbled up in her. She kicked her evening sandals off and let them fall onto the carpet below.

At the door to the bedroom where her luggage had been left, he hesitated, then moved on to his own room. Setting her down, he nuzzled at her throat while his hands tightened around her waist; then they brushed upward to cup her breasts through the thin fabric of her gown.

"This is a fantastic dress," he muttered, mov-

ing his legs a little way apart to cradle her between them.

She gasped softly at the feel of him pressing
against her, then tossed her head back so that
her unruly curls tumbled across her bare shoulder blades. "Worth the special effort?" she
asked breathlessly.

"Oh, yes. And worth removing carefully,
which I'm not sure I'll be able to do in another
few moments."

"Then by all means, let me." Untangling herself from his arms, she stepped back and began
to undo the long row of tiny buttons running
down the low-cut vee of her bodice into a dip
below the waist.

There were some two dozen of them, and by
the time the last fell open, a dull flush stained
Falconer's lean cheeks. His long fingers trembled visibly when he reached out to touch the
creamy skin revealed to him.

"So beautiful... Botticelli couldn't have created a lovelier color or texture."

"I seem to remember that his Venus rising
from the sea was more generously endowed."

"Each to his own taste. As for me..." He
trailed a finger down the cleft between her
breasts, edging beneath the lace-trimmed rim of
the teddy that was all she wore under the gown,
"I couldn't ask for greater loveliness."

The husky caress of his voice mingled with
his touch to send shivers radiating down her
spine. She found it impossible to stay still; instinctively she swayed toward him, her hips
seeking the cradle of his hard thighs.

"Enchantress," he murmured, his broad chest rising and falling swiftly beneath his ruffled evening shirt.

Tyne gasped as his thumb and forefinger closed over her nipple, coaxing it to ultrasensitivity. Each brush of the calloused tips against her heightened her response. Her breast nestled into his hand like a white dove seeking sanctuary.

The first time they had made love, he had concentrated all his skill and strength on pleasuring her; since then they had reveled in the shared arousing and fulfilling of each other.

Now she was determined to take the lead, to express the truth of her feelings for him in the only way she was yet willing to allow herself.

Her hands were quick and deft on his shirt, undoing it and easing it, along with his jacket, away from his wide shoulders and strong arms. She caught both in her hand and eluded his grasp to move away, hanging them carefully over a mahogany valet set in a corner of the bedroom.

Falconer watched her with a bright, fierce light burning in his golden eyes. With her dress hanging open and the silk teddy pushed down to bare one delectable breast, she looked breathtakingly lovely and sexy.

Without haste, Tyne turned off all the lights except the lamp burning beside the bed and plumped the pillows. Only then did she yield to the hunger she saw stamped on his proud features and return to his arms.

But even then she didn't allow him to regain

the initiative. Lightly she stroked his shoulder
and arm with one hand as the other undid his
belt and unfastened the single button on his
waistband.

Pausing, she smiled up at him and brushed
herself against the thick pelt of hair covering his
chest. His thick groan brought a smile from her
as she moved to fuel his desire even further.

The soft, slender hand that slid inside his trousers to cup him gently sent a shock of pure pleasure rippling through him. His hands stroked
through her thick curls, up from the nape of her
neck to rub sensuously over the sensitive skin
behind her ears.

"You're very bold tonight," he muttered as
she brushed against the engorged tip of his
manhood in a feather-light caress he felt to the
core of his being.

"Let's just say I'm inspired."

His eyes narrowed slightly with concern. He
didn't have to ask what had prompted her as-
sertiveness. Both knew that nothing made life
more precious than the nearness of death.

There were harsh realities to their time, perhaps to all times.

In the flick of an instant, life could be snuffed
out.

In the space of a heartbeat, the most fervent
hopes could be dashed.

In a world torn apart by danger, the only
safety lay in love.

Yet to give oneself in love also opened the
way to terrible pain. That was the dilemma they
both had to face. For him, risks were a way of

life. For Tyne, Falconer knew, they were a reminder of terrible emotional vulnerability and
pain.

He could fight mindless fear, blind fate, the
callousness of their materialistic world. But he
was afraid he couldn't fight the shadows of a
shattered childhood that still clouded the eyes
of the woman before him.

Somehow he had to find a way to convince
her that despite all their differences, she could
trust herself to him.

Just then it was becoming impossible to think
of anything except the incalculable delight she
was lavishing on him with her hands and body
and mouth.

"Sit down," she murmured, urging him onto
the edge of the bed. When he obeyed, she finished slipping off her dress, leaving her in
nothing but the disheveled silk teddy.

The fabric of it was so delicate as to be all but
transparent. When she knelt before him to remove his shoes and socks, he could see the delicate line of her spine trailing down to the curve
of her buttocks and the cleft of her thighs.

Dazzled by the sensual spell she wove around
him, he fell back across the bed, drawing her to
him so that her riotous curls spilled over them
both, the honeysuckle scent of them filling his
nostrils.

His touch held the faintest roughness as he
pushed aside the other strap of the teddy and
bared both her breasts to his ardent gaze. Her
nipples were full and hard, the aureolas dark
rose against her alabaster skin. He marveled at

the perfection of her even as she threatened the very limits of his self-control.

"Easy, sweetheart," he rasped. "You're driving me crazy."

She lifted her head, her light blue eyes clear as the air in the high reaches where falcons fly. "I want to. You're usually so disciplined ... so controlled ... but not tonight."

Tonight she wanted to break down all the barriers between them, to take him into her and keep him safe from anything and everything the haphazard future might hold.

And she wanted to prove something to herself, that she could cast off the chains that had always kept her so contained. She would truly reach out, if only this once, to the man who had made her dream that all dreams might be possible.

A lesser man, insecure in his masculinity, couldn't have coped with her sensual aggressiveness. But Falconer gloried in it. He submitted willingly to the magical woman on him, who was in the process bewitched herself.

His big hands clenched at his sides, and his skin gleamed with sweat, yet he made no effort to stop her. Every response of his body—the groans that rumbled up from his chest, the ardent power of his arousal, the ragged pace of his breathing—all proclaimed that he was completely in her thrall.

Tyne's face was tight with concentration as she bent over him. All the secrets she had ever learned about lovemaking were put to ample use, and more were discovered.

The soles of his feet were hypersensitive, as was a particular spot midway up his calves, as was the hair-roughened skin at the apex of his groin just below his flat, hard abdomen.

Stroking her tongue around his navel made his hips lift toward her; feathering a touch over the muscled arch of his ribs caused shivers to race through him; blowing lightly on the nest of downy hair beneath each arm made him moan her name.

Fascinated by him, enthralled by her power, driven to greater and greater heights, she put aside all thought of her own satisfaction in her single-minded drive to ensure that this night would be forever imprinted on both his body and spirit.

It was an act at once of affirmation and defiance. Life flowed between them, glorious and unfettered. Death was banished into the dark shadows that grew more and more distant as an incandescent light filled them both.

Like the rustle of leaves on a sultry summer night, the first faint wafting of what was to come whispered through her. It blew like a hot wind over still water, raising peaks that grew ever higher. Something wild and free called from deep within her, an ancient sound of recognition and welcome.

Fierce in her concentration, she straddled him, rubbing the silk-covered center of her womanhood against his long, hard arousal. The tormenting pleasure tightened within them both, bringing them so close to the furthest limit of endurance.

Teetering on the edge of control, Falconer gasped. Reaching a hand down between her legs, he unsnapped the delicate garment and bared her to him. Though she trembled convulsively with the force of her passion, she waited a moment longer, balancing on the very tip of him until slowly, ardently she drew him within her and made them one.

11

"I'M NOT SURE I survived that," Falconer murmured a long while later, when passion had stilled to warm contentment and they lay cuddled against each other in the big bed.

Tyne laughed throatily. A benign haze of relaxation and peace had permeated every cell of her being and bestowed on her a decidedly rosy glow. "Are you complaining?"

His arms tightened around her. "No way! You pack a delightfully potent punch, woman."

"Hmm...you aren't so bad yourself." She rubbed her cheek against the thick curls covering his chest and sighed contentedly. "I'll admit now that I was a little afraid you would think I was being too aggressive. But you sure did handle it well."

"Sweetheart, you can be aggressive with me anytime," he murmured tenderly. "I'll never try to restrain or confine you."

Tyne's eyes were fluttering closed even as she nodded sleepily. "I know...falcons have to be free."

He smiled against the silken smoothness of her hair. "Is that what you are?"

"Must be...." She giggled softly. "You know

what they say about birds of a feather flocking together..."

Quick images flitted through his mind: Tyne lying naked on the grass in the field above the lake where they had first made love; riding Dancer into the wind with her magnificent hair flying out behind her; walking gracefully toward him in her gypsy dress, challenge in her every step.

Yes, there was something of the falcon in her, just as there was in him. Perhaps that was why they had managed to find each other amid the vast reaches of the earth and sky.

But the proud birds didn't always fly. Sometimes they sought the protection of their high eyries, where nothing could touch them except the hand of God.

Pulling the covers up more securely over them both, he drew her into the shelter of his body as he murmured, "Remember, falcons know how to nest."

Tyne was already asleep and didn't hear him.

THEY SLEPT LATE the next morning and woke to the distant sounds of lunchtime traffic making its way along the avenue far below.

Falconer turned over lazily, smiling even before he opened his eyes. He breathed deeply of Tyne's sleep-warmed scent and felt the smoothness of her naked body against his.

Her hair lay in a riot of curls over the pillow they shared. Through the red-gold strands, he could make out her closed eyes, the thick fringes lying across her cheeks, the spattering of freckles over her nose. Her lips were slightly parted and looked a bit swollen, reminding him of what had passed between them in the night.

He shook his head wonderingly. Would she ever cease to surprise him? All his experience told him that a woman had few secrets, if any, after the establishment of intimacy. Tyne was very much an exception. The more he knew her, the more he sought to learn about her.

Careful not to wake her, he slipped from the bed and walked over to the armoire set against one wall. In it he found a terry-cloth robe, which he slipped on.

Glancing out the window, he noted that the day was clear. Strollers from the office buildings and apartment houses that ringed the park were out in force, some meandering along the tree-lined paths, others gathered in the open fields to sunbathe or play desultory games of Frisbee.

He smiled to himself as he moved soundlessly from the room, intent on ordering brunch and deciding what they might do with the rest of the day. Tempting as it was to think of spending it in bed, he also felt the urge to be out and about with her, sharing the pleasures of a world that suddenly seemed far more promising.

When his call to room service was completed, he stretched out in an easy chair with a thermos of hot coffee, thoughtfully left by a hotel employee, and a copy of the morning's newspaper. He was turning to the financial pages when the phone rang, and he rose swiftly to answer it before Tyne could be disturbed.

As it happened, the absence of his warm, strong body cuddled against hers had already brought her to wakefulness. While he was taking the call from Prince Abdul, she was in the bathroom, brushing her teeth and washing her face, while trying to summon the courage to go looking for him.

Even as she rather sternly told herself that it was ridiculous to feel bashful at this late date, she hesitated before confronting him. If he said or did anything to make light of their passion, she would be deeply hurt.

His expression was completely serious, even somber, when she joined him in the living room. So much so that she shivered slightly, wondering what had happened.

"Falconer, is something wrong?"

He looked up slowly, his eyes shuttered. "What . . . ? Oh, no, nothing." Rising, he crossed the room to her side, dropped a quick kiss on her mouth and managed a smile. "You're just in time. Brunch should arrive any minute."

Tyne nodded, but continued to watch him carefully. Despite his denial, she was convinced something was out of kilter, perhaps very much so. And she couldn't shake the dismaying thought that it had something to do with her.

"Did you sleep well?" he asked as he pulled out a chair for her at the table and filled a cup with steaming coffee.

"Of course," she blurted out before she could stop herself. "Didn't you?"

He grimaced at his own lack of tact as he joined her at the table. "I'm sorry, darling, I wasn't thinking." The timbre of his voice dropped slightly, becoming warm and caressing. "Last night was magnificent. You're an incredible woman."

Tyne didn't think for a moment that he was lying to her, but she couldn't shake the sense that he had far more on his mind than what they had shared. Yet despite her cautious efforts to learn what might be troubling him, she was unsuccessful, at least at first.

Brunch arrived—seafood crêpes, honeydew melon and spinach salad for her, a steak with eggs for him. They laughed at the disparity in their tastes, and the atmosphere grew a little more relaxed, though still shadowed by something she couldn't define.

The meal was almost over when at last Falconer said, "I've been thinking about what we might do today."

"It doesn't matter to me," she assured him quickly, wondering if it would be too bold to suggest they stay in the apartment.

"Perhaps not, but it does to me." His sudden seriousness drew her up short. They were back to the mood he had been in earlier.

Tentatively she said, "Something is obviously bothering you. I wish you would tell me what it is."

Barely were the words out than she held her breath, afraid she might quickly have cause to regret them. There was, after all, no permanency to their relationship. None at all. Perhaps the previous night had finally satiated his desire for her, and he wanted to let her down gently.

Instead he did just the opposite. "I've been thinking about the future and how much I want to share it with you."

Shock twisted through her, only to be followed by joy she couldn't bear to acknowledge. That would be pretending that dreams really came true, something she couldn't afford to let herself imagine.

She looked away, fighting for control. Her efforts were shattered when he aked quietly, "Tyne...have you ever thought about getting married?"

Her coffee cup clattered against the saucer. "I—is that a purely theoretical question?"

"No."

"Oh...." Surely she was misunderstanding him? He couldn't possibly mean what he seemed to.

"Well, uh, let me see...marriage...yes, I guess I've thought about it from time to time. After all, people do get married, don't they? Quite often, as a matter of fact. Sometimes the same people, over and over." She knew she was babbling but couldn't seem to stop.

"Some marriages work," he pointed out quietly.

"How many? In Connecticut, where I live, it's less than two out of three. Those aren't good odds."

"I realize there are risks involved, but—"

"And even if a couple does stay together, how

often are they really happy? Some people just tolerate each other for the sake of the children, or whatever."

And some people were beyond such problems and concerns, cut off from even the chance of happiness. People dwelling in the shadows. Like her.

"I realize we haven't known each other very long," Falconer was saying, "but I understand myself well enough to know when something is right for me. Being with you—in all ways—is the best experience I've ever had. I don't want it to end."

The swift, empty answer that sprang to Tyne's lips died unsaid. She couldn't brush off what he was telling her, no matter how upsetting that might be. His obvious sincerity demanded better of her.

"Look," she said slowly, "this isn't easy for me. I've never been in a situation like this. . . ."

"I know." He smiled reassuringly across the table. "Neither have I."

He *didn't* know; in fact he had no idea. She could hardly tell him that. Instead she said, "We're still strangers to each other."

"You really believe that?"

"I have to; it's true."

"Not to me."

How could she argue with that? He seemed so convinced. Sighing, she shook her head wistfully. "I only wish things could be the way you want. But I know they can't. Life just isn't like that."

"Life is what we make of it. A very wise man

said once, 'The best way to predict the future is to invent it.'"

"Unless the past intervenes."

The words hung between them, a barrier that couldn't be overcome. Falconer didn't make the mistake of trying. "You mean your parents?" he asked gently.

Silently she nodded. Her hand felt cold under his. He wanted to warm her and felt a stab of futility at the thought that she might not let him.

"Eventually you have to let go of the past," he said.

She met his eyes. "Another very wise man said that those who forget the past are condemned to relive it."

"I'm not talking about forgetting, only about going on."

"I am, in my own way."

"And you've achieved a great deal," he acknowledged.

Tyne's fingers tightened under his. "What do you mean?"

"Your writing, of course. What did you think I meant?"

He was watching her very carefully. She resisted the urge to glance away. "There's a certain measure of safety in being an observer of the world rather than a full participant." Safety she had never truly known.

Falconer hesitated. She thought he was about to say something; then he seemed to think better of it. After a moment, he said, "Safety can be a kind of prison, especially when it doesn't leave room for dreams."

She thought of his castle and how it seemed at first glance to provide a haven against the turbulent world. Yet the sense of sanctuary was misleading; reality had to be held off with guards and gates, and even then it could intrude at any moment.

"Falconer," she murmured, "as you said, we haven't known each other very long. I don't think we should rush into anything."

He leaned back in his chair, the terry-cloth robe falling open slightly over his chest. She looked away, refusing to be distracted.

Grimly he said, "What is it you're afraid of, Tyne? That you're not good enough for me or . . . is it the other way around?"

"What are you talking about? That has nothing to do with anything."

"Of course it does." He shoved back his chair and stood up. With his hands clasped behind his back, he strode over to the window, stared out for a long moment, then turned to face her again.

"You've alluded over and over to the fact that you think I'm a dreamer, while you pride yourself on being a realist. But if you're so pragmatic, why aren't you jumping at the chance to marry a very wealthy man?"

"That doesn't even deserve comment. You know perfectly well I don't need you or any man to support me."

"Why not? You could have complete material security for the rest of your life. That's nothing to turn your back on so easily. But you're willing to do so, because deep down inside

you're every bit as much of a dreamer as I am."
Gently he added, "You're a romantic who wants
to marry for love."

"I'm not even sure what love is supposed to
be," she protested, "except for what we've
shared the past few days, and that was simply
physical."

"The hell it was! Don't try to tell me that you
haven't been involved emotionally, because I'll
know you're lying."

Tyne grasped the arms of her chair, her
knuckles turning white. She didn't understand
how they had fallen into this argument, but she
knew she wasn't about to let him speak to her
like that.

"You think you know me so well, but on what
basis? A few days spent together, a few confi-
dences shared? That isn't much." Her mouth
curved in a mirthless smile. "You wouldn't buy
a company you knew that little about; how am I
supposed to believe you'd make what's supposed to be a lifetime commitment based on
it?"

"Because I'm telling you so! If you'd actually
listen to me, instead of hearing what you think
you want to, you'd have realized that by now."

"Don't tell me I don't listen! I'm a reporter, I
make my living listening!"

"Then why don't you start!" Striding over to
her, he glared down angrily. "Damn it, I'm in
love with you! What does it take to get that
through your thick head?"

"You don't know anything more about love
than I do! You're caught up in some romantic

fantasy, and you expect me to just go along with it."

"That's nothing but an excuse, and you know it! I'm a hell of a lot more familiar with reality than you ever will be. I damn well understand enough about it to realize that the idea of making a commitment to someone who doesn't fit your restricted little vision of the world scares the hell out of you!"

Tyne had taken all she could. Her face was pale and her eyes glinted as she rose, drew herself to her full height and faced him. There was ice in her voice. "What scares me is this idea you seem to have that I can be manipulated."

He stared at her, anger giving way slowly to wariness. "What are you talking about?"

"Do you really think I'm a fool? Why did you choose this morning to bring up the subject of marriage?"

"After last night . . ."

"The truth, Falconer. Last night was special, but it couldn't have made you jump the gun like this. If there's one thing I've learned about you, it's that you're a very patient man. You would have picked your time better."

That was the problem with dealing with an intelligent woman, Falconer thought grudgingly. It was damn near impossible to hide anything from her. He started to say something, thought better of it, and stared at her silently for a moment before finally slumping back into his seat.

All his skill and experience at negotiation were proving useless in this case. He had gambled that he would be able to find some way to bind her to him quickly, and had failed.

Quietly he said, "There's no point in our yelling at each other. That doesn't accomplish anything."

She nodded cautiously. "I agree." Sitting down opposite him, she said, "We're both adults. We should be able to deal with this reasonably."

"Yes, by all means, let's be reasonable."

Frowning at his sarcasm, she shook her head wearily. "I'm not good at playing games. Please tell me what this is all about."

He wasn't much good at games, either, it seemed. Before her resolute determination, he had no defense.

Meeting her eyes, he said quietly, "Abdul called this morning. The final points of the treaty have been ironed out. You're free to go get the story now."

12

FALCONER TOOK THE HELICOPTER back from New York and headed straight for the stables to saddle up Pegasus. As he did so, Dancer nickered at him pleadingly. He paused long enough to stroke the pretty mare's nose, wishing he could reassure her—and himself—that everything would be all right.

He wasn't at all certain of that. He had sprung that business about marriage on Tyne with no warning, acting out of desperation when he realized their time together was about to end, when so much still remained unsaid.

Desperation was something he hadn't had much experience with in recent years, and he had responded to it badly. The mere thought of doing without her made him ache deep inside. To avoid the pain, he was willing to sacrifice a lot. Perhaps even survival, had he but known it.

Damn it, he should have stayed in bed and made long, slow love to her. That at least might have put her in a more receptive mood. But no, he'd shot his mouth off and sent her running.

As he collected the falcon who had been growing stronger with each passing day, he wondered if Tyne's interviews were over yet. Probably. She would have known exactly what questions to ask and no doubt had gotten the answers she wanted.

He smiled faintly, wondering if the secretary had figured out yet what had hit him. Abdul probably hadn't. He had called again before Falconer left town to say he was looking forward to meeting with Tyne.

"She's remarkable, my friend," the prince had said appreciatively. "Beautiful, intelligent, discreet. Truly the perfect woman."

"Don't get any ideas," Falconer had growled before he could stop himself. "She's also taken."

His friend had chuckled indulgently. "Is she? Somehow I got the impression Miss Saunders is very . . . independent."

"You don't like independent women."

"I could change my mind."

"Don't."

That single word had told the prince everything he wanted to know. His laugh had been deep and rich. "It's good to see you finally fall, my friend. As our old proctor at Exeter used to say, 'Make a better man of you.'"

Falconer had uttered a short, explicit response to that and hung up. He was in no mood to endure Abdul's good wishes, no matter how sincerely meant. Especially not when he knew there might be no basis for them.

Pegasus shied beneath him, sensing his tension; the hooded falcon responded by arching his wings. Falconer reined in the stallion and rubbed his neck to calm him while speaking softly to the bird. All the while wishing his own anxiety could be banished as simply.

They continued on for several minutes before he realized he was instinctively heading toward the field where he and Tyne had made love. Cursing impatiently, he cut through a copse of oak trees bordering the river.

The day, so clear that morning, was beginning to cloud over. Absently he noted that thunderheads were gathering toward the west. He'd have to watch them.

It was cooler by the river. He relaxed the reins and let Pegasus wander freely. The horse seemed pleased to be out and about. He didn't like confinement any more than his rider. Leaning forward in the saddle with his hands resting on the pommel, Falconer stared out over the water. His gaze was focused inward, on a landscape of dreams through which he no longer wished to journey alone.

"YOU JUST MISSED HIM, ma'am," the stable boy said. "Mr. Darcourt went for a ride 'bout half an hour ago."

"I see..." Tyne murmured. "Could you saddle Dancer for me while I get changed?"

The stable boy nodded.

Smiling her thanks, Tyne hurried up to her room and quickly stripped off her clothes. It took only moments to pull on jeans, a shirt and boots. When she was done she burrowed her way to the back of the closet and removed the loose panel.

Someone had been in her room since she'd last used it. Someone who had left Argus's

calling card; a high-powered rifle with telescopic site. Lifting the businesslike weapon, she
inspected it. The automatic pistol she carried
was intended for self-defense; this was another
matter entirely. The rifle served only one purpose, to kill from a considerable distance with
lethal efficiency. In the hands of a sharpshooter,
which she was.

The metal felt cold and heavy in her hands as
she slipped the ammunition clip into place. Automatically she confirmed that the telescopic
site was correctly aligned, the silencer attached.
Only then did she replace the weapon in the
soft leather bag where she had found it.

The bag in hand, she left the room quickly.
She was back in the stable yard before the mare
had a chance to become impatient.

Which was more than she could say for herself. As she started off, Tyne thought about the
odds of finding Falconer on the large estate and
grimaced. He might have gone in any direction;
she could search all day without success.

Fortunately it had rained the night before.
She was able to make out the freshly turned
clods of earth on the river path. Urging the
mare on, she tracked the stallion's trail.

The storm coming up from the west caught
her attention. It was moving in fast, which
made it likely Falconer would turn back. She
rounded a bend in the road, hoping to spot him,
but did not.

A finger of lightning cleaved the sky over the
hills. Dancer whinnied nervously, and Tyne

spent some moments comforting her. The crack of thunder that followed seemed to echo all around them.

The ensuing silence was all the deeper by contrast, until it was interrupted by the first few splashes of rain against leaves.

Tyne had always enjoyed a good storm, but this one worried her. It would make her job all the more difficult.

FALCONER KNEW HE SHOULD TURN BACK, but he wasn't anxious to do so. The wild weather suited his mood. Perhaps it would obliterate for at least a little time the tumult raging within him.

Unlike most horses, Pegasus also liked the rain. He pranced under his master, expressing his enthusiasm. Falconer laughed and lifted his face to the sky. Cold drops of rain pummeled his face. He closed his eyes and let the water wash away his dread.

ON THE HILL ABOVE, the assassin watched. The automatic rifle was aimed, silencer in place, the trigger cocked.

The horse shied; the target moved out of range. No sound escaped the assassin, no indication of impatience. Slowly, methodically, the weapon was realigned.

In the cross hairs of the telescopic sight, the tall man with golden hair showed clearly. His eyes were closed, his face lifted to accept the benediction of the rain.

And whatever else fate might hold over him.

A finger closed around the trigger once again and squeezed.

FALCONER LOOKED DOWN at his chest in surprise. Raising a hand, he touched his shirt. His fingers came away wet and sticky.

Instinct drove him to the ground, pulling Pegasus with him. Sheltered behind a fallen rock, he raised his head just far enough to survey the landscape. The falcon had leaped from his wrist and was climbing into the leaden sky, but in what seemed to be slow motion. By contrast, the light was fading fast, much more quickly than he would have expected, even with the storm.

He heard a buzzing noise like a bee's . . . and shook his head to clear it. The stain had spread all the way down his chest. Blood was dripping onto Pegasus's silken mane.

TYNE RAISED the rifle slowly. Her arm was absolutely steady, her breathing even. She might have been on the target range, so emotionlessly did she view the tableau before her. But her calm was deceptive; buried deep within, desperate emotions struggled to be free.

She couldn't let that happen, not while the mission still remained to be completed.

Once again she sighted down the long barrel of the automatic weapon. Once again she checked the ammunition clip. Everything was just as it should be. Nothing remained except to pull the trigger.

Dancer nickered softly behind her. Tyne ignored the sound, as she did the rain that had turned her hair and clothes to a sodden mass. Her skin was cold, but she didn't shiver. No movement, however slight, would be allowed to disrupt her aim.

The man moved below her. He was crouched low to the ground, trying to make his way without being seen as he searched out a new position for a better shot. A clump of rocks gave him temporary refuge, until he moved beyond them. He was making for a copse of trees near the river. Tyne decided he wouldn't make it.

She waited for the space of a single heartbeat. Then she fired.

13

"You carried out your mission perfectly," the most senior of the three people seated around the table declared. "We are very pleased."

"We understood the difficulties," the woman next to him added. "This was hard on you."

"Yet you came through as always," the younger man on her right said. "Argus thanks you."

Tyne heard them out in silence. Instead of the usual postmission debriefing she had expected, she had found herself summoned in front of this triumvirate, the day-to-day administrators of the secret organization she had served for so long. They were also the highest-ranking members she had ever come in direct contact with. The experience was disconcerting to say the least.

"Falconer Darcourt was an extremely difficult subject," the woman was saying. "Very intelligent, independent, even iconoclastic. We admire the way you handled him."

"I didn't." The words were little more than a whisper, but the three people gathered around the marble table heard them nonetheless. They looked at her curiously.

"What do you mean?" the elder man asked.

Tyne hesitated. She didn't want to explain, or

discuss, or in fact do anything that would keep her in the room a moment longer than absolutely necessary. And yet she could hardly refuse to answer.

"I think you already know what I mean," she said slowly, scanning their faces one by one as though the answer might be seen there. Their expressions were unrevealing. Resigned, she went on, "I didn't 'handle' Falconer. From the first moment we met, I began to lose my objectivity about him and about the mission. In the end, it was all I could do to complete it."

"Still, you did so," the younger man pointed out. "Very successfully."

When Tyne didn't respond, the three exchanged glances. A moment passed before the woman asked, not unkindly, "Surely you don't regret what happened?"

"No . . . I only wish there could have been a chance . . . for something more."

"Argus teaches that there is always a chance, provided proper action is taken. Isn't that, after all, the entire basis of our organization: to shape the future rather than merely let it happen?"

Tyne smiled sadly. How could she explain to these pragmatic, even ruthless people that while forceful action worked well enough in the real world, it had no place in dreams? They required far gentler handling.

What it all came down to in the end was the essential difference between Falconer and her. He was an idealist, a man who saw the world as he believed it could be. She was a pragmatist, seeing the world as it was. For him, there was the castle and the hope of a better tomorrow. For her, there was Argus and a battle that seemed never to end.

"You seem rather tired," the older man said gently. "Perhaps we should arrange a leave of absence."

"That might be a good idea," Tyne murmured. "I have the treaty story to write...and my notes on Falconer need to be turned over to another reporter to do the profile on him. Then I would like to get away." As far as she could, though it wouldn't be far enough. The thread of memory was infinite.

"THANK YOU FOR YOUR TIME, Mr. Secretary," Tyne said as she shook hands with Hiram Griswald at the conclusion of their interview.

The silver-haired diplomat nodded. "My pleasure, Miss Saunders. Frankly, it isn't all that often that I'm interviewed by such a charming and, shall we say, effective reporter."

Tyne smiled politely. The meeting with the secretary had gone extremely well, as had the earlier interview with Prince Abdul. She was ready to write what might well be the best story of her reporting career, but she couldn't muster the least enthusiasm for it.

"We'll be announcing the treaty to the media at large in about twelve hours," Hiram said as he escorted her to the door. "I trust that will give you ample time to get your story written and in print."

"Yes, it will." Dutifully she added, "I appreciate the exclusive."

"We appreciate your discretion. It made all the difference."

"This was very much an exception," she told him honestly. "Generally speaking, I'm against any reporter holding back on a story."

"I understand that. But if news of the negotiations had broken early, they would have been completely derailed. As it is, we now have a real chance to stabilize the situation in the Mideast."

Tyne expressed her hope that that would turn out to be the case, then said goodbye. As she left the State Department and made her way out onto the street, she reflected that she wouldn't mind a little stability in her own life.

That train of thought could only lead to futile regrets and diminish the concentration she needed so badly. Discipline, so carefully instilled over so many years, enabled her to put wishful thinking aside, with difficulty.

Reaching the offices that the *Financial Times* maintained in the capital, she settled down at a borrowed desk and got started.

Writing was generally hard work for her, done in fits and starts with nothing flowing smoothly until the final polishing was completed. This was different. She batted out the story with less effort than she would a shopping list, yet when she had gotten through the first draft she already knew it was very good.

Tyne shook her head at the irony of this happening to her just when she had been wondering if she would ever get enough of a grip on herself to write anything, much less a cogent, hard-hitting article.

Chauncey called when she was about half-way through. "How did it go?" he asked without wasting time on preliminaries.

Punching a "save" command into the word processor, she said, "Fine. Both the secretary and the prince were very cooperative."

"They damn well ought to be, considering how you helped them out."

"Y-you knew about that...?"

He chuckled. "When are you going to get used to the fact that you can't put anything over on your old editor? It was obvious when you dropped by my office that something big was in the works."

Guiltily remembering that she had been more concerned about his discovering her relationship with Falconer, she murmured, "It's a great relief to have it out in the open."

"Oh," Chauncey said innocently, "is it?"

"I hate to cut you off, chief, but we'll be breaking the story in the next edition, won't we...?"

"Hmm, yes, of course. Better get back to work, then. We're holding a good chunk of page one for you. Just one other thing," he added. "When will you have the Darcourt story for me?"

"Uh, we need to talk about that. I think it would be better for someone else to take over."

"I thought that might be the case," he said simply.

"It seems that I got . . . too involved."

"That happens, to the best of us."

Tyne appreciated his understanding, but she hoped he wouldn't pursue the topic. Chauncey seemed to realize that, for after a moment he said, "Of course, since you were a witness to what happened, we'll want you to give a statement."

"Of course."

"That's fine, then." He cleared his throat. "Now finish the treaty story and hop on the next available plane. You'll undoubtedly want to be somewhere nice and quiet when we scoop the networks."

That was true enough, Tyne reflected a short time later as she put the finishing touches on the article, then switched on the modem that connected the computer to the telephone and transmitted her work to New York.

Half an hour later, Chauncey had approved it for publication. She was packing up, preparing to leave for the airport, when the phone on the desk rang.

Absently Tyne picked it up. "Saunders."

"This is Hiram Griswald, Miss Saunders. Have you finished writing the story?"

She was surprised to hear from him. "Yes, just now. Why? Was there something you wanted to add?"

"No, I just have a message for you. Your leave of absence has been arranged."

Tyne's hand tightened on the receiver. Loose ends were suddenly falling into place: the automatic pistol smuggled into her room shortly after her arrival at the castle, her curiosity about who had brought Argus into the matter in the first place, her annoyance at her own selection for the mission.

Quietly she asked, "You've known Falconer a long time, haven't you, Mr. Secretary?"

"Yes, we go back quite a ways."

"I see.... So you knew how difficult it would be to put someone in really close to him?"

"Extremely; he's a very private man."

"But still a man...."

Her unspoken question hovered in the air. Softly the voice at the other end of the line acknowledged, "There was a high level of probability that the two of you would be attracted to each other."

Tyne's mouth tightened. "I don't appreciate being used like that."

"That was never the intention."

"Then what was?"

The secretary hesitated a moment. She could hear the faint scrabbling of electrical impulses along the line. That and her own breathing.

At length he said, "Intention is perhaps the wrong word. Hope would be better."

"I don't understand...."

"You don't want to. It takes great courage to face the world as it really is, but even greater courage to dream." He paused, then added quietly, "And the greatest of all to love."

Was that what Argus had wanted her to learn, Tyne wondered as she put the phone down. Since the brutal death of her parents twenty years before, the organization had cared for her, taught her, given her a purpose in the world. But it had never managed to heal her.

Was that the true mission?

If so, it was not yet over.

14

"GOOD AFTERNOON, MISS SAUNDERS," Winston said. "It's nice to see you again."

"It's nice to be back," Tyne returned with equally grave politeness. The social amenities taken care of, she got down to business. "How is he?"

The security chief restrained a grimace. "Uncomfortable, but refusing to admit it."

"The doctor had no luck convincing him to go to the hospital?"

"None. He insists the wound is minor."

Tyne's light blue eyes flashed ominously. "For a supposedly intelligent man, he can show all the common sense of a squirrel."

Winston's mouth twitched. "Rather less than that, I suspect."

They shared a sympathetic glance. "I'd like to see him," she said.

"Of course. We were finally able to get pain-killers into him, so he may be asleep. I'm sure he wouldn't mind your going on up, though." On the contrary, the security chief's expression made clear; only her departure had been amiss, not her return.

Tyne understood that, though she didn't dwell on it. She hurried up the stairs, making no at-

tempt to dismiss her anxiousness. When she
reached the door to Falconer's quarters, she
hesitated.

They hadn't had a chance to talk after the
shooting. She had no idea how he felt about what
had happened. Most particularly, she didn't
know how he felt about her now that he knew
the truth, or at least a large portion of it.

There was only one way to find out. Remembering what Hiram had said about courage, she
opened the door quietly and walked in.

The room was dimly lit, the curtains drawn
against the late-afternoon sun. It took a moment for her eyes to adjust. When they did, they
were drawn irresistibly to the figure in the bed.

Falconer lay on his back, his eyes closed and
his breathing slow and regular. The covers were
pulled up as far as his waist. Above them his
broad chest was bare, except for the large white
bandage that covered most of his left side.

Were it not for the bandage, it would have
been impossible to guess what had happened to
him. His coloring was good, and there was no
trace of fever.

Tyne's hand shook slightly as she drew it
from his forehead. Try though she did, she
couldn't quite suppress the memory of those
terrible moments when she had come upon Falconer in the copse and realized that all the efforts of the security forces—the government's,
his own, Argus's—had come perilously close to
failing.

All along they had presumed that Falconer
was relatively safe so long as he remained

within his castle, and that the danger to him would end when the treaty negotiations were concluded.

Tyne had feared otherwise. With hindsight she understood that her special feelings for him had heightened her perceptions and honed her instincts to a razor sharpness. She had followed him to the castle because Argus had said to stay near him. But she had taken Dancer out because she couldn't bear to be parted from him, even briefly.

When she had seen him lying wounded behind the rocks, she had thought of nothing except the fierce need to protect the man she loved.

To do that she had been willing to kill. And she had had the means. But she had also realized that Falconer might never be completely safe unless the details of the plot against him—and against the treaty he had helped to bring about—were known.

Sitting down on a chair beside the bed, she studied him quietly as she reflected on the price of courage. It had cost her dearly to hold her fire and take slow, steady aim until she was certain she would only wound the would-be assassin.

Even then, the man was immensely danger- ous. He was a fanatic eager to die for his cause—and appalled not only because he had been stopped from carrying out his deadly mission, but also because a woman had been the agent of his defeat.

He had lashed out at Tyne as she approached, only to be subdued with swift, remorseless skill. She had no time to waste on him, not while Falconer lay bleeding.

He was conscious enough, at least intermittently, to realize what had happened. Yet he said nothing, only watched her with hooded amber eyes as she sent Pegasus racing back toward the stable. Then she administered first aid that the doctor later said had saved his life.

By the time the helicopter arrived, Falconer had fainted from loss of blood. Tyne told herself that was just as well. She had dreaded the thought of having to face him and hear him condemn her duplicity.

In retrospect, her decision to leave seemed cowardly. But there was a limit to anyone's courage. Hers had been stretched to the breaking point.

Now, as she sat there beside his bed, she knew she would never have been content to stay away. Not after what he had asked of her.

For better or worse, she had to have a chance to answer.

FALCONER SLEPT through the rest of the day and into evening. Tyne remained at his side, content to simply be near him. About an hour after her arrival, Winston knocked on the bedroom door. When she opened it, he asked quietly, "Can I get you anything?"

"No, thank you." She stood aside to let him in and gazed at the man in the bed. "He's sleeping very deeply."

The security chief nodded. "I wouldn't be

surprised if he's settled down because you're here."

"He doesn't know, though. He's been asleep since before I arrived."

He smiled at her gently. "If the positions were reversed, don't you think you would know?"

Tyne considered that, her eyes never leaving Falconer. Winston was right; she would be aware of his nearness under any circumstances.

After a moment, the security chief said quietly, "I have some news."

Tyne went with him to the door, where they could talk without fear of disturbing the sleeping man.

"The terrorist talked," he explained. "It seems that when he realized he hadn't bought his ticket to paradise, he lost his enthusiasm for the cause. The group he belonged to was very small and obscure. They were rounded up without any great difficulty."

"So you think that's the end of it?"

"As far as Falconer is concerned. There are certainly other groups that will oppose the treaty, but they're going to have their hands full coping with the effects of it." He smiled with grim pleasure at the prospect.

Tyne nodded, unsurprised. Argus didn't always win, but the organization's success rate was high. Over time she didn't doubt that it would prevail.

When Winston left a short time later, Tyne took a quick shower before returning to the bedroom. Falconer was still asleep. Wrapped in one of his robes that she had found in the dressing room, she sat down beside him once more.

The events of the past two days had drained her strength. Almost before she realized it, her eyes were beginning to close. With a sigh she gave into temptation and slipped into bed beside him. Moments later she, too, was asleep.

WHEN SHE AWOKE it was daylight. Birds were chirping outside the tall windows. A soft breeze blew through the cracks in the curtains. The last remnants of the storm had blown away, leaving behind clear blue skies.

Tyne sneezed. Her throat burned, and her head felt stuffed with cotton wool. She sneezed again and fumbled for the box of tissues on the bedside table.

"Sounds as though you've got a cold," a deep voice said.

In the midst of blowing her nose, she froze. Falconer. Awake and apparently in full possession of his faculties. She turned to him slowly, and with as much dignity as she could muster, murmured, "Good morning."

"It does seem so." Propped up on one elbow, his chin in the palm of his hand, he smiled lazily. "I'm glad to see you're here."

"You are?"

There was no mistaking her skepticism, but Falconer didn't comment on it. Instead he said, "It saves me the trouble of having to go after you."

Tyne stared at him. He seemed to know what

he was saying, yet she couldn't help doubting his words. Perhaps he was delirious.

"Are you in pain?" she asked worriedly, straightening up. The robe she had fallen asleep in slipped open slightly, revealing the curve of her breast. Her hair fell in curls around her shoulders. The color matched the redness of her nose.

"I'm fine," he assured her.

"You lost a lot of blood."

"I would have lost considerably more if you hadn't come along when you did."

The mention of her role drew Tyne up short. She didn't feel prepared for the questions she knew must be coming, but she couldn't think of a way to avoid them.

Resigned, she reached for a fresh tissue. "I suppose you realize now that I was sent to guard you."

"I did manage to figure that out," he murmured dryly.

"Your determination not to bow to the terrorists made you especially difficult to protect."

"So I've been told."

"Somebody had to be brought in without your knowing."

He nodded gravely. "Somebody I wouldn't suspect of being an agent?"

"Right." How she wished he wasn't. With very little effort, all her actions after arriving at the castle could be interpreted in the worst possible light.

Quietly Falconer asked, "Tyne, was it part of your job to make love with me?"

"Of course not!" Anger and hurt tore through her with equal force, much as she had thought herself prepared to deal with such an accusation.

Telling herself fiercely that her eyes were watering because of her cold, she said, "I would never, under any circumstances, do what you're suggesting. Moreover, the organization I work for would never ask such a thing of me. Although—" She broke off, belatedly aware that what she was saying wasn't quite the truth.

"Although . . . ?" he prompted. Sitting up in bed, the covers falling around his waist, he looked at once extraordinarily virile and vulnerable. His thick golden hair was disarrayed, and a night's growth of beard darkened his square jaw.

To Tyne's bleary eyes, he was irresistible.

"They seem to have known we would be attracted to each other."

He raised an eyebrow. "Did they?"

Embarrassed, she looked away. "I'm afraid so."

"Well, they were certainly right about that, weren't they?" On a more reflective note, he added, "I wonder what else they were right about."

"What do you mean?"

"Never mind. This organization, do you like working for it?"

"It's the only life I've ever known. Even my writing came about because of those people." His silence urged her to go on. "They took me in after my parents died. I had no other relatives, so it was fairly simple to get custody of me."

"Were they kind to you?"

"Exceptionally so. I was very ill for a while. The aftereffects of shock, I suppose, coupled with a small child's sheer inability to cope with that sort of savagery. Anyway, they took very good care of me. I never felt dehumanized, or anything like that."

"So you grew up wanting to repay this... agency?"

"Yes, but there's much more to it. We live in a very dangerous world. It sounds corny, but someone has to be willing to fight the bad guys."

Falconer nodded thoughtfully. His side ached slightly, and he was still tired from the loss of blood, but none of that could dim his awareness of the woman beside him. He wondered if she had any idea how lovely she was, or how much he loved her.

Love. He had never really hoped to experience it. Now that he was, he understood that it was nothing like some poets might imply, all hearts and flowers, sweetness and light.

On the contrary, love was a dark, molten force within him. Like the fiery blood of the inner earth that, once freed, threatened to deluge everything in its path.

Everything except the knowledge that he could never bear to hurt the woman who watched him so apprehensively. He had already made one mistake with her, when he had pushed too hard to try to get her to reveal what he had prayed were her true feelings. This time he would go much more carefully.

"Tyne," he said gently, "if you didn't make love with me as a way of staying close, then why did you?"

Her attention seemed focused on the long sleeves of his robe that drooped over her hands. Slowly she folded each back. Only when that was done did she respond. "I was very attracted to you."

"Sexually?"

"Yes." Honesty compelled her to add, "And in every other way. Sexual desire has never impressed me as sufficient reason in itself for intimacy."

"It isn't," Falconer agreed softly. "True intimacy rests on a great deal more."

Tyne smiled wistfully. "So I've discovered. But for intimacy to be sustained, people have to be very well attuned to each other. They need a shared view of the world."

"I think I'm beginning to understand.... You're still convinced that I'm a dreamer and you're a pragmatist and never the twain shall meet. Is that it?"

Tyne gripped her hands together. She avoided answering directly. "Yesterday you saw me shoot a man. How did that make you feel?"

"Relieved," he said promptly. "It was a classic case of 'better him than me.'"

Tyne shook her head. "It's only natural to react like that, at first. But weren't you also shocked and even... horrified?"

"Do you mean were my idealistic sensibilities

offended? Was I cruelly disillusioned to discover that the beautiful, gentle woman I had
come to know had such a different side to her
nature?''

The acerbic note in his voice surprised her.
She tried to comprehend it, failed, at least for
the moment, and went on to other things.

"Not just that. Most people confronted by a
threat will go to great lengths to prevent it from
being carried out. They will also try to steer
clear of the uglier parts of life, to create some
sense of security around themselves, however
nebulous it may be.''

She spoke without apology, even knowing
how he would interpret her remarks. Falconer
didn't turn his back on the harsher realities of
the world, but he did insist on confronting
them on his own terms. Terms she thought
were dangerously idealistic.

That judgment showed clearly in her eyes; he
didn't mistake it. Holding her gaze with his
own, he said, "You seem to have forgotten that
this time we won. The treaty exists, and it will
make a difference.''

"And you almost paid with your life," she
pointed out tightly. "That's where dreams can
lead to.''

Falconer bit back a hasty retort. He got out of
bed, ignoring the discomfort in his side, and
strode across the room to pull open the curtains. Sunlight flooded through the high windows.

"You shouldn't do that," Tyne protested, trying not to stare at him. His broad shoulders and

back tapering down to lean hips, sculpted buttocks and long muscular legs were all most distracting. Absently she sneezed again.

"That's a nasty cold," Falconer said as he turned to her. Standing silhouetted against the window, he looked very large and very inscrutable. Yet his words couldn't have been more mundane. "Maybe we'd better get the doctor back."

"Would you listen to yourself? All I've got are the sniffles, whereas you—" She broke off, abruptly aware that she was going to cry and desperate not to do it in front of him.

Quickly she slid out of the bed. "You need to rest, and I'm keeping you from it."

Falconer's response was swift, but Tyne was swifter still. She might have made it to the door first, except that she tripped over the hem of the robe that hung down well past her ankles.

A low, fluent imprecation broke from her, prompting an admiring whistle from Falconer. "That's some vocabulary you've got."

"It's expanding by the minute. Has anyone ever told you you're an absolutely infuriating man?"

"It's been hinted at."

"Take my word, it's true." She sniffed again and cast a quick glance at the door.

"You're a good one to talk," Falconer grumbled as he reached her side. His gaze was unexpectedly gentle. "You realize this is the point in the story when I should sweep you off your feet, carry you off to bed and make wild love to you until you forget about everything else?"

He grinned abashedly. "Unfortunately, neither of us is in shape for that. So do you think you might give me a rain check and come back to bed on your own?"

As he spoke, he was drawing her into his arms, which rather had the effect of preempting the debate. Just as well, Tyne thought groggily. She could barely see straight, let alone think, and those damnable tears would no longer be restrained.

"I may want to invest in a tissue factory," Falconer murmured as he wiped her cheeks.

"You probably already own at least a dozen."

"Here. Blow."

"I'll do it myself."

"Don't argue. Just blow."

"That's another thing about you," she muttered after grudgingly doing as he said. "You're too used to getting your own way. We'd fight all the time."

He leered cheerfully. "Think how much fun it will be making up."

She grimaced at the cliché and tried to prevent him from unfastening the robe. Somehow the effort was beyond her, and before she quite knew how it had happened she was lying naked beneath the covers, nestled in his arms against his uninjured side.

"There's something I think I'd better point out," he said softly.

"What's that?" Her voice was thick from the cold and weariness. She had her eyes closed, so she couldn't see the look of utter tenderness that lit his eyes.

"You saved my life, so from now on you're responsible for it."

Her thick lashes quivered, lifted. Blue met amber. "You don't really believe that."

"Cross my heart and hope to—"

"Don't." She caught the hand that was about to move over his chest. "Don't say it."

His mouth touched hers, tentatively. "I'll tell you what, we'll compromise. If you won't agree that you're responsible for my life, would you mind very much agreeing to share it?"

"Mind?" The husky sound that came from her throat was somewhere between a laugh and a sob. "No, I wouldn't mind." Hesitantly she added, "I was afraid you would reject me after you learned who I am."

He was silent for a moment, stroking her bare back in an instinctive gesture that soothed even as it aroused. "To reject you would be to reject myself. You said we didn't really know each other, but that isn't true, at least not for me. I know I'm in love with you and always will be."

Tyne couldn't be less courageous than him. Besides, lying in his arms, warm and safe, her defenses were cracking wide open. Truth was moving irresistibly toward the light.

She took a deep breath and murmured into his bare shoulder, "I love you, too." Before he could respond, she went on quickly, "For the life of me, I wish I didn't."

Her cheeks were damp again. He wiped away the tears with the calloused tips of his fingers and listened with a full heart as she said, "You have to understand. I loved my parents, and I lost them. I'm afraid the same thing will happen to you.''

His arms tightened around her. "Because I'm an idealist determined to reform a ruthless world?''

She nodded mutely. Beneath her cheek, she could feel the accelerated beat of his heart. Odd, but she could have sworn that relief was what he was feeling. "Go to sleep,'' he murmured tenderly. "We'll work everything out later.''

"Dreamer.''

"Always,'' he answered, but she was already asleep.

15

"COULD YOU TELL ME where to find Mr. Darcourt?" Tyne asked of the first servant she encountered when she left her room. She had slipped in there to get dressed, after waking to discover it was afternoon and Falconer was gone.

"I believe he's feeding the peacocks, ma'am, in the formal gardens," the young man said politely.

Tyne thanked him and hurried off. The nap had cleared her head. She felt much better able to think and to cope.

So what if she and Falconer seemed to look at life from opposite points of view? They loved each other. It wouldn't be easy, but perhaps they could find some resolution to their differences. At least their relationship was worth the effort.

To concentrate on her fears instead of her blessings would be the worse sort of self-betrayal.

That was uppermost in her mind as she reached the gardens and scanned them for some sign of him. She found him almost immediately, standing near a tall yew hedge. Half a dozen gloriously plumed peacocks clustered around him, their tails fanned to reveal dozens of the characteristic iridescent eyes, in the golden light.

It was a pleasant, even bucolic moment, yet something about it disturbed Tyne. She had taken several steps across the lawn when the scene seemed to shift slightly, as though a frame of film had come suddenly into focus in her mind.

The sun was behind Falconer, silhouetting him against the sky. It made him seem even taller and broader than he really was. From where she stood, with the ground slanting up toward him, he looked almost like . . . a giant. . . .

She stopped, her face expressing surprise, disbelief and, at last, stark comprehension.

Falconer glanced up. He started to smile, only to break off abruptly. Wariness flooded through him. Brushing the last of the grain from his fingers, he walked toward her. Their gazes locked. "You've figured it out," he said.

She nodded numbly. "I don't understand why it took this long." Her stunned gaze fell to the peacocks. Almost to herself she murmured, "In Greek mythology, the peacocks got their eyes when a giant with a hundred eyes died and no longer needed them."

"The giant, Argus," Falconer confirmed softly. "The strong, far-seeing guardian."

How could she herself have been so blind, Tyne wondered? It wasn't as though there had been no clues.

His superb physical conditioning, for one, and his self-defense expertise. His familiarity with the corridors of power, through which he himself walked with ease.

His dream of a better world—not, as she had feared, the chimera of one man pitting himself against overpowering odds, but the guiding vision of a worldwide group of immensely skilled and determined men and women who stood ready to back him in everything he did.

Although no one within the organization spoke of him directly, it was well known that all major decisions were made or at least approved by one person whose identity was Argus's most carefully guarded secret. And yet, that person still wouldn't necessarily know everything that went on within Argus. Especially when others who held him in great loyalty and affection were determined to protect him, even from himself.

Falconer had even mentioned a succession of "odd jobs" that Winston had refused to enlighten her about. He had suggested she ask Falconer.

"When did you first become involved with Argus?" she asked quietly.

"In Vietnam. I was in the Special Forces there, along with Winston." He smiled ruefully. "It was right after my father died. I was as green as they come. Winston kept me alive."

"He says you saved his life."

Falconer nodded reluctantly. "That's true, I suppose. Winston was badly hurt in a firefight and we missed the last helicopter out. I was trying to find out somewhere for us to hide so that we wouldn't be captured, or worse, when this guy came along in a jeep and offered us a lift."

He laughed. "He asked as though it was the most ordinary thing in the world. Next thing I knew, we were pulling up to an airstrip outside the village. There was a plane sitting there. That was so extraordinary, given the time and place, I could hardly believe it was real. But it was, with every seat taken by guys like Winston and me, who had figured their luck had run out. They made room for us somehow."

"Par for the course," Tyne murmured, "for Argus."

"That's right, although it was a while before I understood that. After I got out of the service, the guy who had picked us up stayed in touch. He made a few suggestions that helped me get my business off the ground. Looking back, I realize he did a lot more than that, but no one has ever mentioned it, not even to this day. It wasn't until ten years ago that I was formally recruited."

There were people who had been with Argus far more years, some as many as half a century, since the wisdom born of experience was highly prized. But it still wasn't surprising that Falconer was now responsible for them all. He had the special combination of ability and vision that made him ideally suited to lead.

The few very oblique references she had heard to the person at the top of Argus had been transmitted with intense respect bordering on reverence. It amused her to think that, even so, the organization would contrive to put one over on its chief.

"You had no idea I was coming?" she asked softly.

Smiling, he shook his head. "None. I'd been so insistent about not being smothered by my own security that I guess my seconds-in-command decided there was no further point in trying to reason with me."

"So they took matters into their own hands, without even informing Winston? He is one of us, too, isn't he?"

"Of course, but no, not even he was told. Although I suspect if he had been, he would have cooperated fully." His eyes lit on her gently. "He's informed me that if I let you get away this time, he'll wash his hands of me."

"I find that difficult to believe." Tyne's mouth quirked at the corners. She had always liked Winston; it had just taken her a while to realize that. "It was rather presumptuous of them to think we would be attracted to each other."

"Yes," Falconer agreed with a wry smile. "Good thing for them they were right."

She ignored that, for the moment. "Why didn't you just tell me straight out once you realized who I was?"

Falconer's expression sobered. "Because I know how strongly you feel about Argus, and I didn't want you confuse those feelings with your feelings for me."

Tyne started to protest, then thought better of it. He did have a point. Even if she hadn't confused them, he could never have been absolutely sure of that. Still, he might have said *something*.

"You let me go on and on about the differences between us and how difficult they would be to overcome," she protested, unable to hide her hurt and bewilderment.

Instantly he crossed the small remaining distance between them and took her into his arms. Against her hair he murmured, "I'm sorry, but I couldn't deny what you were saying. I am the idealist you accused me of being, and you are far more pragmatic. The point is, there's room for both. In Argus and in our lives."

Tyne believed him. She could hardly do otherwise when everything in her was proclaiming the absolute rightness of all they shared. The hurt of a moment before faded. In its place was tremulous joy and the burgeoning belief that perhaps all things truly were possible.

"How is your side feeling?"

Surprised, he said, "It's fine. Why?"

Her eyes lifted meaningfully to the clear blue sky. "Looks to me like we're due for rain."

Falconer laughed, a deep, rich sound that made the peacocks arch their combs and strut more swiftly. "You're absolutely right. Could be a downpour."

"I'd hate to get caught in it."

"With such a bad cold? I couldn't possibly permit that."

Her nose wrinkled in feigned concern. "Don't tell me you're going to get dictatorial."

"Me? I wouldn't dream of it. We'll discuss our differences and compromise." As he spoke, his eyebrows drifted upward, investing the ordinary words with a deliciously lurid suggestiveness.

"Hmm...sounds good." Slipping an arm through his, she laughed softly. The sound rose to the sky, where a falcon soared on rivers of golden light.

MUCH LATER, lying sated in the circle of his arms, Tyne murmured, "Poor old Chauncey. He'll have a fit when he hears we're getting married."

"Will you keep on writing for him?" Falconer asked, trailing a lazy finger down the curve of her cheek. The smallest detail of her fascinated him. He could see without difficulty down the long passage of years to come and knew that his enthrallment would never end.

Tyne was thinking much the same. "I do enjoy it a great deal. Besides, it's a perfect cover."

"Hmm...one thing about that, sweetheart." He twined a curl of titian hair around his fingers. "I would greatly appreciate it if you could see your way clear to accept a transfer within Argus."

"Let me guess—away from field work to something sedate, like planning and operations?"

"You read my mind."

She shifted against him languidly, breathing in the warm, musky scent of his skin. "I could be persuaded."

He smiled in the gathering twilight. "My pleasure. Suppose I spend our honeymoon doing that?"

"I could think of worse ways," she admitted, nestling closer to him. "Did you have anywhere special in mind?"

"Abdul has kindly offered to lend us an island of his in the Mediterranean."

"That sounds lovely, but if I might suggest an alternative ... ?"

"Of course. Didn't I say we'd compromise?"

"You did, and you do, wonderfully. Now about that honeymoon ..." She glanced around at the alabaster stone walls of the castle, sheltering them from the darkness and the cold. "Let's stay here instead." He was already agreeing as she added joyfully, "After all, this is where dreams come true."

This month's irresistible novels from

— TEMPTATION —

UNDERCOVER by Maura Seger

The guards had locked Tyne Saunders in a cell and thrown away the key. No one knew this was all part of Tyne's plan . . . she wasn't both an ace reporter and a crack shot for nothing.

It was Falconer Darcourt, the high-powered business-man she was sworn to protect, who threw her into turmoil. Suddenly she was deeply involved with him, in bed and out. She couldn't afford to feel this way —distracted and in love—when Falconer was in so much danger. . . .

LOVE THY NEIGHBOUR by JoAnn Ross

Dr. Laurel Britton's move to Phoenix was eventful, to say the least. Her runaway piano dented a Ferrari —owned by her next-door neighbour, the handsome but furious Nick McGraw!

Then, her first day on the job at the Sports Clinic, Laurel discovered Nick was her patient. More sparks flew between them—this time of a decidedly erotic nature. Laurel tried to keep their relationship on a professional footing. But with his sensual glances and teasing kisses, Nick seemed to have other ideas. . . .

SUMMER SURRENDER by Abra Taylor

Christy Sinclair had expected to find tutoring Dr. Joshua Brent's motherless daughter challenging. But the passionate advances of her explosive, magnetic employer proved much more difficult.

The longer Christy remained in Joshua's secluded seaside home, the harder it was to recall the well-ordered life she had planned with her fiancé. For the tumultuous desires Joshua's masterful hands aroused in her traitorous body were so new—and close to raging out of control. . . .

Spoil yourself next month
with these three novels from

—TEMPTATION—

UP IN ARMS by Lynn Turner

Two problems met Erin Sutton when she assumed her place as head of the SuttonSport empire. First was a longtime employee challenging her authority. Second was the virile Texan Jeffrey Brandt, her new design engineer.

Power plays Erin could handle. But the dangerous sex appeal in Jeff's arsenal of devastating qualities posed a real threat to her self-control. And outside the office, Erin felt at a distinct disadvantage. . . .

A WOMAN'S CHOICE by Rita Clay Estrada

Sam Lewis, attorney-at-law, was immediately attracted to Catherine Sinclair—despite her lethal reputation with men. The blonde, blue-eyed siren had tearfully requested his help . . . and soon devastated him with her sensuous appeal.

But Sam's feelings for Catherine ran deep—beyond merely protecting her from a very real threat. He wanted her in his life, in his bed. And he wanted her in spite of her questionable past. . . .

EMBRACE ME, LOVE by Cathy Gillen Thacker

Eileen Garrett had worked hard to be a super mother to her young son, Teddy. Then Teddy found a new hero—Little League coach Ross Mitchell. Ross was everything Eileen could want in a man—gentle, strong, devoted to her son. And in his arms she felt dizzying waves of desire.

Eileen wanted desperately to trust Ross's words of love. But first she would have to test his promises. . . .

Look out for these books
already published by

Mills & Boon

—TEMPTATION—

If you experience difficulty in obtaining any of
these titles, write to:
Mills & Boon Temptation, P.O. Box 236,
Croydon, Surrey CR9 3RU.

Readers in South Africa write to:
Mills & Boon S.A. Pty., Postbag X3010,
Randburg 2125, S. Africa

To be read with caution whilst sunbathing.

The Mills & Boon Holiday Pack contains four specially selected romances from some of our top authors and can be extremely difficult to put down.

But take care, because long hours under the summer sun, engrossed in hot passion can amount to a lot of sunburn.

So the next time you are filling your suitcase with the all-important Mills & Boon Holiday Pack, take an extra bottle of After Sun Lotion.

Just in case.

PRICE £4.40 AVAILABLE FROM JUNE 1986   Mills & Boon